THE ILLUSTRATED ENCYCLOPEDIA OF

MINERALS
& ROCKS

THE ILLUSTRATED ENCYCLOPEDIA OF

MINERALS & ROCKS

By J. Kouřimský

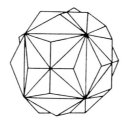

Page 2: Sphalerite — Cavnic
(Romania); actual size of crystals
up to 12 mm

Page 4: Amethyst — Porkura
(Romania); actual size of crystals
up to 4 cm

Page 5: Basalt pit — Rovné, near
Semily (Czech Republic)

Designed and produced by Aventinum Publishing House,
Prague, Czech Republic

Text by Jiří Kouřimský
Translated by Vera Gissing and Václav Sochor
Graphic design by Karel Drchal

This edition published 1995
by Sunburst Books, Deacon House,
65 Old Church Street,
London SW3 5BS

ISBN 1 85778 088 4
Printed in the Czech Republic
3/23/02/51-01

CONTENTS

Mining in the Middle Ages; woodcut from the work of G. Agricola 'De re metallica', 16th century

From time immemorial, humans have been attracted by the enchanting beauty of the shape and colour of minerals. The primitive human, unable to understand some of the properties of the beautiful stones, often saw something supernatural in them. People even believed that some stones had the power to help them change their destiny, a belief which has survived until the present time.

Minerals are among the most beautiful products of nature, and the number of those who admire and collect minerals is increasing. This is in spite of all the difficulties of mineralogy, the science of minerals. To study minerals means to know the fundamentals of chemistry, physics and a number of other sciences. Crystallography alone is difficult and many have been discouraged from studying mineralogy, even as a hobby.

This book is intended as an introduction to mineralogy; at the same time, it is an attempt to provide a compact survey of the basic data. The book is not very theoretical but offers many interesting facts from all areas of mineralogy. The relationship of humans to minerals is examined in some detail and the basic mineralogical and geological terminology, whose knowledge is essential for any true enthusiast, is clearly explained.

The chapters on the different elements and compounds form the core of the book, each of the main minerals being included in its particular chapter on the basis of the latest scientific system. Chemical composition, key physical characteristics, data on origin, on occurrence, and also on past and present uses are shown for each mineral. Thus a survey is given of the most important ores and non-metal materials, as well as precious and decorative stones. With some minerals, special attention is given to the history of their discovery and often an explanation is given of their names as well as other interesting information.

This book will enable you to see and understand the wonders of the mineral world which can bring so much joy and satisfaction to any keen observer.

1   Diamond monstrance (with 6,222 diamonds) — in the Treasury of Loretto Monastery (Prague) 89.5 x 70 cm; Viennese work, 1699

People all over the world have always tried to unveil nature's secrets and exploit its riches for their own benefit. Culture and civilisation have been influenced by nature from the dawn of human history until the present time.

Humankind's relationship to mineral resources is a significant measure of the extent of cultural development at any time. An important indicator is the skills used in working and processing the mineral raw materials. The link with rocks must have been as significant for primeval humans as for people today. Primeval humans could turn a rock into a tool or weapon. Ancient Egyptians exploited ores and used stones to build cities. People of the 20th century extract a number of metals and use various minerals as building materials and fuels.

Primitive people had no tools nor clothing and their needs were few. The first mineral of importance to them was rock salt. They found salt deposits when following the instinctive behaviour of animals around their home. Later, they learned to use their hands and brains in processing rock as a raw material.

During the Stone Age, people used rocks for tools and weapons. At first they used pebbles and chippings of rock such as limestone and sandstone. However, they soon discovered that it was better to use sharp-edged quartz, flints or obsidians, which they sharpened or chipped. By the end of the Stone Age, they discovered copper ores and melted copper in open fires and later in furnaces.

When humans discovered tin ore (cassiterite) in alluvial deposits they learned about the advantages of combining copper and tin: they realised that bronze, the alloy from these two metals, had more useful properties than plain copper. This marked the birth of a new era in human history — the Bronze Age. The use of bronze spread from the valleys of the Nile and Euphrates to the Mediterranean region. However, as copper and tin were expensive materials, rock continued to be used for making the common tools. Meanwhile, the importance of stone as a building material was growing. The first stone palaces were rising in the valley of the Nile and in Mesopotamia, and in Egypt limestone blocks of immense weight were used for building pyramids.

The Iron Age began only 3000 years ago. Extracting iron from ore is more difficult than smelting copper and tin because much more heat is needed. Attention was drawn to iron ore by its conspicuous blood red colour. The ore was melted with charcoal to obtain iron as a cheap substitute for the expensive bronze. The discovery of iron metallurgy initiated an unprecedented advance of human activity in agriculture and crafts.

Iron became the most widely used metal in the Middle Ages. Iron ore was at first extracted from pits, later from shallow mines. The miners in the Middle Ages used extremely simple tools but the mining techniques gradually improved. The old deposits in areas that had belonged to the Roman Empire were exhausted and abandoned and new ones were sought. An expansion of iron ore mining began at the time of Charlemagne (742-814) in France and also in central Europe — in Bohemia, Saxony, Slovakia and Styria. Relics of mining activities have remained in such places until the present time.

Abundant information is available on the minerals extracted in the Middle Ages, on the mining techniques used and on the location of the main deposits. We owe this to Georgius Agricola (1494-1555), a distinguished physician and mineralogist, who spent part of his life at Jáchymov, Bohemia. (Jáchymov was, at Agricola's time, one of the most important European centres of silver mining.) Agricola's key works are his writings

2   Large emerald
mounted in a piece of
jewellery, used as
turban decoration (El
Kassir, Egypt); Turkish
work from the 17th to
18th century

De re metallica libri XII (loosely translated as *Twelve Books on Mining and Metal-lurgy*) and *De natura fossilium libri X* (*Ten Books on the Nature of Stones*). These are, in fact, the first scientific works on mineralogy, geology and metallurgy.

As industrial manufacturing flourished, increasing amounts of ores, fuels and raw materials were needed for metallurgy, for the chemical, glass, ceramic and building industries, for the manufacture of stoneware and refractory products. Even farmers began to use mineral substances (as fertilisers). The extent and effectiveness of utilisation of minerals have been increasing and mining methods have been improving up to the present day.

Some materials are referred to as 'strategic'. These include materials which are essential for the safety of nations. Of course, what is strategic at a particular time depends on the latest achievements of science and technology. For example, iron ore mining is no longer as important as centuries ago, nor is the mining for the metals needed to make high-grade steel so important as fifty years ago. The present-day strategic raw materials include ores of radioactive substances, ores of light metals (for the aerospace industry), petroleum and some minerals of less obvious importance such as diamond.

The practical use of rocks and minerals for industrial purposes is just one aspect of people's relationship to stone. People have always been fascinated by the beauty of some minerals. They have gazed at the shape of crystals whose origin they could not explain, and it is not surprising that sometimes they thought the crystals held supernatural powers. Even in the Stone Age, primitive humans became interested in gold, which was easy to melt and cast. It is from gold that the first pieces of real jewellery were made. Silver was mined along with copper during the Bronze Age for the same purpose. Jewels, ornaments and religious statuettes were also made by ancient peoples from less 'noble' materials such as copper and bronze, or from rocks of unusually striking colour or shape. Exquisite ancient gold jewellery and other golden objects have been found in regions of the world where the metal was in abundance, for example in Peru and Mexico.

The first use of precious stones and the beginnings of their exploitation as mineral materials date back to prehistoric times but it is not known which nation worked them first. The oldest reports come from India and from the countries of the eastern Mediterranean, where precious stone deposits were located. Other well-known deposits are in Sri Lanka (rubies, sapphires), in the Island of Zebirget (St. John) in the Red Sea (olivines) and in south-eastern Egypt (emeralds). The engraved gems on the Babylonian-Assyrian seal rolls originate from the 4th millennium BC.

The working of precious stones spread from the Orient to Greece, where the art of gem engraving — glyptography — originated. The Romans enhanced the knowledge of precious stones: they acquired the working methods from the Greeks and gathered further knowledge from the nations of Asia and North Africa. The oldest Roman gems (precious stones cut inwards — *intaglia*, or in a raised form — *cameo*) have been found in Etruria (Tuscany) and show the influence of Egypt. The Roman stonecutters were mostly Greek in origin; they founded their workshops mainly in southern Italy. The first work of Pliny the Elder (died AD 79) on natural history gives details of the deposits of precious stones and describes the shapes of crystals. Pliny also mentions that the Roman Emperor, Nero (AD 37-68), used an emerald spectacle lens, which is in fact the first reference to the technical use of a precious mineral. After the disintegration of the Roman Empire, the art of precious stone working moved mainly to Byzantium.

In the early Middle Ages the ownership of precious stones (particularly in Europe) was confined to rulers, high nobility and dignitaries of the Church. The art of working

3 Filigree of gilt silver with almandine (Asia Minor) and with turquoise (Iran); Ottoman work from the 18th century

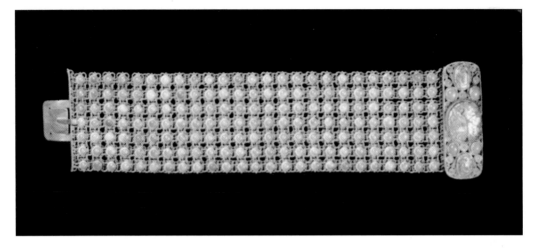

stones declined after the disintegration of the Roman Empire. This was due, to a large extent, to the new philosophical trend which viewed the world and its values in a different light. Early Christianity, unlike the previous philosophical outlooks, turned from life on this earth to life after death. To be adorned with jewels, which seemed so natural to the heathen in the prehistorical era as well as in the highly cultivated ancient world, was now considered an extravagance. During that time many deposits of precious stones remained neglected. It appears that in the early Middle Ages many methods of working precious stones that had been commonly used in earlier times were forgotten in western and central Europe.

In the Gothic period of the Middle Ages attention was focussed primarily upon rough work on transparent and translucent gemstones. These were never used in their natural state. The stone cutters removed any imperfections from the mineral and gave them at least a superficial polished finish. This process remained rather primitive for a long time, not only because of the poorness of the techniques used but also because of the effort to preserve as much of the stone as possible.

The expansion of the arts all over Europe during the 12th to 14th centuries triggered off a new interest in working stones, first in France and later in other European countries. There was also a renewed interest in trading with gemstones, and large cities through which routes from the eastern stone deposits led became centres of importance. Baghdad and Cairo were the most noted ones. The treatise on precious stones written by an Arabian merchant, Ahmed ben Jusuf al Teifassi, in the 13th century contains a complete list of precious stones and their prices in markets of the Near East.

In the 14th century, especially in the period of Emperor Charles IV, Prague became an important centre of European glyptic art. This was a period of intensive searching for precious stones in Bohemia and the stones were worked in numerous workshops. The art of working precious stones reached its peak in Prague in the 17th century when the city became the seat of Emperor Rudolf II, head of the Holy Roman Empire of the German nation. Stones were brought to Prague from all parts of the world and famous artists and scientists gathered at Rudolf's court. It is therefore not surprising that essential information on precious stones, including descriptions of the stone-working craft and gemstone trading, can be found in a book published in Prague in 1609. This book, *Gemmarum et lapidum historia* (*History of Precious and Common Stones*) was written by Anselmus Boëtius de Boot, a Dutchman by origin, personal surgeon of Emperor Rudolf II, who was a versatile scientist and a great expert in precious stones.

During the second half of the 17th century, the baroque style penetrated into art and influenced all life. Monumental buildings were constructed, emphasising the power of the Church and feudal nobility. Taste changed, and so did the perception of luxury. The new fashions demanded vast quantities of so many types of stones that glass imitation stones were often used to satisfy the demand.

Not until the second half of the 18th century did society start to look at precious stones in a different light, influenced by the new philosophic doctrine, rationalism. The increasing wealth of scientific and technological knowledge brought about a change in people's relationship to precious stones. A new class of society rose to the fore, and these people became interested in jewels and in valuable objects not only for their personal adornment but for financial gain. The stone-working craft began to flourish again mainly in the second half of the 19th century. The large sums of money spent on stones

5 Detail of gold malachite set (the Urals); Viennese work from the beginning of the 19th century

brought more capital to the industry. The ever-growing demand necessitated the search for new deposits and for discovering new types of gemstones, which had not been used until that time.

In the last decades of the 19th century and during the 20th century, the popularity of precious stones was, to a large degree, determined by fashion. Attractive natural gems were very much liked and high prices were paid for them. The successful production of some synthetic gemstones caused a temporary threat to the natural stones. Particularly in the 1920s many people wore so-called imitation jewels. However, it was not long before the popularity of natural stones returned and, at present, genuine gems are highly prized again.

BASIC CONCEPTS

Mineralogy is the science which studies minerals. It not only observes and defines the various characteristics of minerals but also explains their origins and changes.

A mineral is a chemically and physically homogeneous inorganic natural substance, usually a solid but occasionally a liquid, of a definite chemical composition. Natural substances have developed by natural processes; hence, minerals as natural substances do not include products such as synthetic gemstones, made artificially by chemical reactions, or slags which develop during metallurgical processes. As said, minerals are homogeneous, which means that all particles in the mineral are chemically and physically alike. In this a mineral differs from rock, which is also an inorganic natural substance but consists of different minerals. Rock, however, forms large compact parts of the Earth's crust (granite, basalt, gneiss). There are some rocks, for example marbles, limestones or quartzites, which consist almost entirely of one mineral, but we do not classify them as minerals because they often form whole series of strata and are not necessarily homogeneous. The science which studies rocks is called petrology.

Mineralogy has two branches: general mineralogy and systematic mineralogy. General mineralogy studies and explains the properties of minerals and observes their various physical and chemical characteristics. Systematic mineralogy studies and describes minerals and includes them in a system on the basis of their internal structure, chemical and physical characteristics and mutual relationships. Both mineralogy and petrology belong to the geological sciences. Geology itself is concerned with the structure, composition and evolution of the planet Earth.

PROPERTIES OF MINERALS

The majority of minerals can, under certain conditions, form smooth-faced pieces — crystals. A closer look at crystals shows that some crystallised minerals nearly always form the same shapes. It is then possible to conclude that the crystal shape is not accidental but is determined by certain laws. The shape is the result of a regular arrangement of the smallest constituent particles. This internal pattern, forming the

7 Clay siderite with animal remains — Mšecké Žehrovice, near Kladno (Czech Republic); Celtic work, 200 BC

structural lattice, also determines the physical properties of crystallised substances.

Though some minerals crystallise only into certain shapes, the structure of many crystallised minerals varies. However, all these shapes follow the same symmetry, which is in line with the group symmetry of the smallest particles of the substance. Hence, the symmetry of an external shape of the crystal is, in fact, an enlarged copy of its internal structure, which is characterised by regularly repeating equivalent surfaces, thus meeting the condition of homogeneity of the mineral. They may therefore have only some elements of symmetry. According to this symmetry, crystals are split into seven major groups, called crystal systems, which can be derived from certain axial crosses. These are: triclinic, monoclinic, orthorhombic, tetragonal, hexagonal, rhombohedral, and cubic.

Crystals do not always develop into a perfect shape under natural conditions — for example, they often fail to grow regularly in all directions. However, in spite of any distortions the angles between the faces always remain the same. Hence, the interfacial angle as an absolutely constant quantity provides the key data for the study of crystals. The surfaces of large crystals are usually striated and may be roughened, druse-like and lustreless. Distortions of some crystal faces, which develop either during the growth of a crystal or through the effects of weathering, are typical of many minerals and may therefore be an important aid in identifying them.

The speed of growth of crystals is among the most important factors underlying the quality of the developing crystal faces. Generally it can be said that the slower the growth of the crystal the more perfect its surface and shape. Rapid crystallisation produces skeleton-like crystals. Crystals of minerals with a simpler chemical composition and minerals free of impurities are usually more perfect and also have a smaller num-

8   Gold brooch with Bohemian garnets (central Bohemian highlands); 4 x 3 cm; Bohemian work, end of the 19th century

9 Jasper — Ciboušov, near Klášterec nad Ohří (Czech Republic); a disc from the reign of Charles IV, 1341, Prague Castle; actual size of the disc 6 cm

ber of faces. This is why the gem varieties of minerals are usually better developed than the common forms.

The physical conditions under which crystals grow have a substantial influence on the shape of the crystals of any mineral. These include temperature and pressure and also the characteristics of the material which surrounds the growing crystal. Crystals which originate in a soft and yielding environment, in which they can easily grow and spread, usually form perfect faces and are generally well developed. Perfect crystals also originate in rock crevices where they are deposited from solutions (waters), vapours or gases. The growing crystals cannot develop faces on the rock surface to which they adhere; they can continue in their growth only on the remaining sides. These are called *grown crystals*.

Various characteristic forms of calcite crystals:
a) rhombohedron, b) scalenohedron, c) columnar crystal

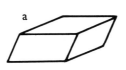

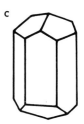

10 Agate brooch —
(Giant Mountains,
Czech Republic)
with garnets (central
Bohemian highlands);
5 x 3,5 cm; recent
Bohemian work

Druses are clusters of crystals growing from a common base in fairly parallel lines. The clusters which develop in round crevices are *geodes*. Geodes occur mainly in crevices of some igneous rocks, especially melaphyres, phonolites and basalts. The assemblage of crystals in druses and geodes is usually in a fairly regular pattern. If the crystals grow in an irregular clump and if new crystals grow onto older ones, such clumps are called *clusters*. Clusters frequently consist of multitudes of tiny crystals, often only imperfectly bounded externally. Such clusters are called *crystal aggregates*. Minerals crystallising only in microscopic aggregates are called *crystalline* minerals, as distinct from *crystallised* minerals. *Lump* minerals are, in essence, fragments of large crystals.

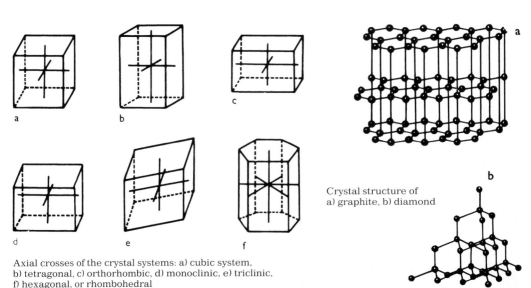

Crystal structure of
a) graphite, b) diamond

Axial crosses of the crystal systems: a) cubic system,
b) tetragonal, c) orthorhombic, d) monoclinic, e) triclinic,
f) hexagonal, or rhombohedral

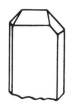

Asymmetrical crystal
of quartz

Structure of hexa-
gonally symmetrical
water crystals
(snow flakes)

Minerals occurring in natural conditions only in a non-crystalline state are much less frequent. These are called *amorphous* minerals.

The growth of individual crystals is governed by definite laws. These laws can often be applied to whole groups of crystals. Such cases are referred to as *regular inter-growths* (twins, triplets etc.) Another interesting mineral form is the *pseudomorph* or mineral mimic. Seemingly crystals, these minerals have an internal structure which is in no relationship with their outer bounding. They may be of different origin, but in all cases they develop as a result of the replacement of the original crystal matter by some other material.

The internal structure of a mineral determines not only its external form but also its physical characteristics. Hence, certain regular relationships also exist between the shapes of crystals and their physical properties. Some of these physical properties, for example hardness, cleavage or optical characteristics, are not the same in all directions in crystallised substances (another fact which is in line with the internal structure). However, there are some properties such as density and radioactivity which do not depend on direction. The main physical properties are described below. Attention is focussed mainly on those properties for which determination does not require special instruments.

11   Pure gold bars; total weight 72 kg

12   Natural sapphires in a timepiece; Viennese work, 1880–1885

Density is defined as the quotient of weight and volume. Density shows how many times a given substance is heavier than the same volume of water at a temperature of 4°C. The greater the content of heavy elements (for example, lead, mercury, silver and others) in the mineral, the greater its weight. On the other hand, the more water the element contains, the lighter it is. Minerals having a stable chemical composition have a stable weight. There are various methods to determine weight, including the use of various balances or immersion of the element in heavy fluids.

Another important characteristic of a mineral is *hardness,* which is basically the resistance of a body to penetration by another body. For individual minerals hardness is determined by Mohs' scale of hardness, which is as follows: 1. talc, 2. rock salt, 3. calcite, 4. fluorite, 5. apatite, 6. orthoclase, 7. quartz, 8. topaz, 9. corundum, 10. diamond. Mohs' scale is only a comparative one, so that the numbers 1 to 10 do not show by how many times a mineral is harder than talc (grade 1, the softest). Special instruments, called sclerometers, have been developed to determine hardness.

Cleavage is closely related to hardness. It is the crystallographically orientated minimum cohesion — a mineral's ability to split, if exposed to external pressure, along certain definite planes in certain crystallographic directions. The perfection of cleavage depends on the mineral and hence may be used as an identifying trait. Cleavage should not be confused with divisibility, which manifests itself as almost planar splits which, however, are not in line with the crystallographic directions. In minerals that are not cleavable, mechanical impact produces uneven surfaces referred to as *fracture,* which may be conchoidal, plane, hackly, granular, etc.

Optical properties make a significant group of physical characteristics of minerals. Some optical properties may be assessed by the naked eye, others have to be determined with the aid of instruments. As light falls onto the surface of a mineral, some light

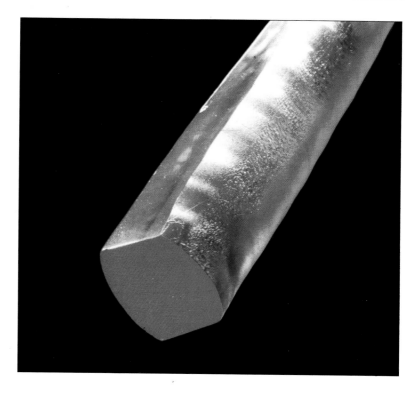

13 Part of synthetic ruby, raw material for manufacture of a laser; diameter 24 mm

beams penetrate into the mineral and pass through it and others are reflected. The more rays that pass through the mineral, the more transparent is the mineral. According to the degree of transparency we distinguish transparent, semi-transparent, translucent, non-translucent and opaque minerals.

Colour can be characterised as a visual perception induced by the impingement of light on a mineral or by its passage through the mineral. Colour, as it is perceived by the eye, is normally the intrinsic colour of the mineral as a chemical substance, but it is often affected by the inclusion of other chemical substances or by mechanical intrusion of a foreign pigment. Sometimes colour is due to a defect of the crystal lattice, which may be caused, for example, by exposure to radioactive radiation. The so-called metallic colours are colours of a special type, which arise as a result the non-transparency and metallic lustre of some minerals. Incident colours are bright interference colours which develop on thin surface layers of minerals by oxidation, intake of water or another chemical change.

Lustre of minerals depends on the quality and amount of light reflected from their surface. It depends on a number of factors, especially the amount of light absorbed by

Various crystal twins: a) gypsum,
b) orthoclase (so-called Carlsbad twin),
c) aragonite

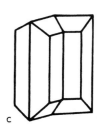

a   b   c

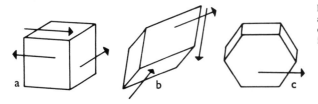

Examples of the varied cleavage of minerals: a) cubic cleavage, b) rhombohedral cleavage of calcite, c) cleavage of mica running in one direction only

the mineral. Lustre is divided according to intensity and quality — minerals have lustres which may be adamantine, semi-metallic, vitreous, greasy, pearly, silky, dull, etc.

Streak, a constant trait of each mineral, is the name given to the colour of the fine powder obtained by rubbing the mineral against a piece of unglazed porcelain, called streak plate. If a hard mineral is to be tested it is necessary to scratch the surface of the mineral with a file or knife.

Radioactivity is an interesting trait of some minerals. It acts very intensively on a photographic plate or film. Various types of Geiger-Müller counter are used to measure radioactivity.

The determination of *luminiscence* may also be used for the identification of minerals. Some minerals, when subjected to short-wave radiation, emit light. Ultraviolet radiation, X-rays or cathode rays are used for the luminiscence test. It is very interesting to observe luminiscence, especially in ultraviolet light, and many mineralogical museums have show cases in which the visitors can watch this phenomenon. At present, many collectors specialise in collecting luminiscent minerals.

14   Stone incrustations with jaspers — Prague Castle, 14th century

15 Detail of stone
incrustations with jaspers,
amethysts and chryzoprases
— Prague Castle

THE ORIGIN AND OCCURRENCE OF MINERALS

As with chemical elements, there is a great diversity in the occurrence of minerals in the Earth's crust. Many minerals (for example, quartz) are present almost everywhere, others occur in a very small number of places. Minerals develop under natural conditions in various ways. One and the same mineral may occur in various associations of minerals (paragenesis) which developed in contact with each other under certain conditions and in a certain geological environment. Hence, the geological aspect, in addition to topography, must be taken into account when the occurrence of minerals is described.

The processes by which minerals are formed can be divided into the following three basic types: magmatic processes (volcanism), sedimentation processes (deposition from water) and metamorphic processes (metamorphism).

Magmatic minerals: the processes that lead to the formation of magmatic minerals can be assessed by the products of the processes (igneous rocks) or can be examined by observing active volcanoes. Magma, the hot molten rock and the basic material of magmatic processes, is a silicaceous melt with volatile constituents (chlorine, fluorine, water vapours and carbon dioxide). It contains sulphur compounds as well as metallic elements. Magma is confined to magmatic foci located in the deep parts of the Earth's crust; scientists believe that the depth of the magmatic foci is more than 6–10 km.

As the Earth's crust moves, or during processes triggered by the overpressure of the volatile substances in the magmatic foci, the magma either effuses to the upper strata of the crust or solidifies as lava on the surface. If the magma solidified beneath the surface of the earth, the rocks that were formed in this way are called *intrusive* rocks. The rocks that developed from the magma that had effused onto the Earth's surface are called *extrusive* rocks. Further, there are also *vein* rocks: these developed from 'blind branches' of magma which solidified in the crevices of the crust.

Intrusive igneous rocks are solidified under the cover of older rocks. They are granular because they have solidified slowly, so that their mineral constituents had sufficient time to crystallise. In the process of the formation of minerals in igneous rocks, an important role was played by the volatile components which were unable to escape during solidification of the magma: they affected the solidification process and also carried rare elements, thus contributing (in the form of compounds in hot solutions or in the form of volatile gases) to the formation of ore veins.

As igneous rocks solidified, the dark minerals, having a greater density and a higher melting point, were the first to crystallise. These include olivine, amphiboles, feldspars with a prevalence of calcium and dark mica. Then followed the light-coloured constituents such as feldspars with a predominance of sodium, light-coloured mica and quartz. From the material around the volcanic vent the molten lava could absorb fragments of rocks which could alter the composition of the original magma. The most common intrusive igneous rocks include granites composed of sodium feldspar, quartz and mica. Gabbroes, for the most part, consist of calcareous feldspars and pyroxenes, and anorthosites are composed almost entirely of calcareous feldspars. Syenites are essentially quartzless granites. Diorites are similar to granite, but dark constituents predominate in their composition.

Extrusive rocks are solidified on the Earth's surface, often in the form of lava. During the effusion of the magma, the majority of the volatile constituents escaped and the rock solidified quickly, so that they are usually fine-grained to glassy. Sometimes the individual mineral components are difficult to distinguish. Globose hollows from the escaped gases sometimes occur in the extrusive rocks; these hollows may be partially

16   Rock salt crystal floating on salt lake — Faiyum (Egypt); actual size 4 x 3 cm

▷

17   Contact colour radiogram of a vein of uraninite — Jáchymov (Czech Republic); actual size 7 x 4 cm

Origin of various types of rocks:
Igneous rocks: a) intrusive rocks,
consolidated at great depths,
b) vein rocks, c) extrusive rocks,
d) pyroclastic volcanic material
expelled from a crater;
Metamorphic rocks: e) f) g) rocks
altered through high pressures
and under high temperatures in
various depths of the Earth's
crust, h) rocks formed by contact
metamorphism from contact
with molten eruptive lava
Sedimentary rocks: i) j) k) l) the
sedimentations of various
geological ages

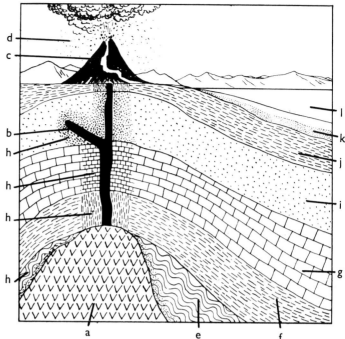

or completely filled with various minerals. Hot springs are the after-effects of volcanic activity.

Basalts are among the most important extrusive rocks. They are, for the most part, of Tertiary origin, dark in colour, having a mineral composition which is similar to gabbro. Phonolites are greyish in colour. Melaphyres are basalt-like rocks of Palaeozoic to Mesozoic origin. The typical extrusive rocks also include volcanic glasses, especially obsidians.

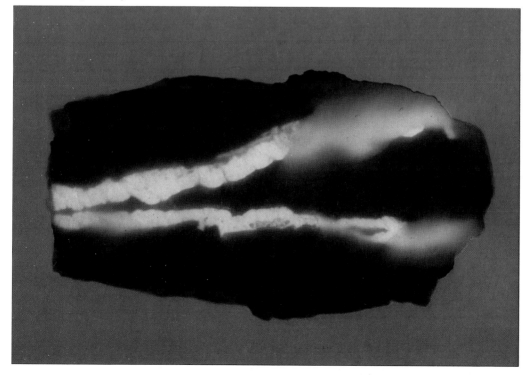

18   Section of rock melaphyre — Želechov valley, near Libštát (Czech Republic); consisting of plagioclase,
hypersthene and olivine. Magnified 11 times.

Vein rocks solidified in the fissures of older rocks and, as such, they are not very thick. They may be both coarse- and fine-grained and often contain what is called porphyric phenocrysts. These are crystals which grew earlier than the remaining matter during the solidification of magma and are therefore perfectly developed. Rocks with such phenocrysts are called porphyries. Pegmatites are another series of typical vein rocks; basically, pegmatites are coarse-grained granites whose development was substantially affected by the volatile constituents of the magma. The volatile substances enriched the rocks with many rare elements; so it is not surprising that pegmatites are among the most significant types of precious stone deposits.

Owing to the after-effects of volcanic activity, ore veins and deposits developed in many places. Ore-bearing rocks developed during the cooling of the originally hot solutions in the fissures of rocks in the upper parts of the Earth's crust at temperatures of 200-400°C. The elements most frequently occurring in the ore veins include gold, silver, nickel, cobalt, bismuth, lead, zinc, copper, iron, arsenic, antimony and mercury. Ore veins are usually tabular bodies but may also have a lenticular or irregular structure. The most common type of ore veins are sulphide veins, that is, veins rich in sulphides. The veins usually originated from igneous rocks, especially granite.

Cassiterite deposits stand between pegmatites and true ore veins. They developed mainly in greisens, rocks similar to granite and composed almost exclusively of quartz and mica. Their formation required comparatively high temperatures (500-600°C).

Long exposure to water, air and the activity of organic life causes erosion of rocks on the Earth's surface. The rocks crumble and water streams carry the grains or larger particles of disintegrated rock to deposit them sometimes very far from the places of their origin. This is how *sedimentary rocks* develop. However, sediments may also be produced by organisms, both animals and plants. Many species of marine fauna have skeletons of calcium carbonate or silicon dioxide. When the organisms die their skeletons gather on the sea floor, producing huge rock strata, such as the series of strata of limestone. Sandstones (hardened sediments of quartz grains) are another common type of sedimentary rock. Slates develop from finer particles.

Metamorphic rocks develop by a different process. No rock remains without changing. The metamorphism is due to prolonged exposure to very high pressure and temperature. The rocks re-crystallise to form new minerals in the new environment. Most of the metamorphosed rocks have a schistose texture and include, for example, gneisses, mica schists, phyllites and other types of schist. The original basic igneous rocks (which are low in silicon dioxide) can turn into serpentinites. Amphibolites are formed in a similar way.

Metamorphism may also occur where existing rocks are in contact with molten eruptive lava. Such a process is called contact metamorphism and the minerals so formed are referred to as contact minerals. Sedimentary rocks most easily yield to the action of contact metamorphism.

Minerals of so-called Alpine paragenesis are sometimes tied to the drusy cavities. We talk about the Alpine type of veins because the cavities filled with finely crystallised minerals occur most frequently in the Alps. Solutions having temperatures below 400°C leached the rocks through which they passed and gave rise to the typical association of minerals in cavities close to the surface.

19   Phonolite deposit with cavities of natrolite — Mariánská Hill, near Ústí nad Labem (Czech Republic)

Chapter 1

ELEMENTS

Abbreviations:

H. = hardness   Sp. gr. = specfic gravity   S. = streak

Elements form a comparatively small group of minerals and occur only rarely under natural conditions. There are 103 known chemical elements but only 22 of them are found as minerals. In reality there are more than 22 minerals in the element group because some elements occur as more than one mineral — for example, carbon occurs as diamond and as graphite.

Pure light metals have so far not been found as naturally occurring minerals. They oxidise rapidly and there are no natural conditions that would preserve them in their pure state. One can say in general that the greater the ability of an element to combine with another, the less is the likelihood of its occurring naturally in a pure form. This is the reason, for instance, why pure iron is far rarer than pure gold, though iron constitutes more than 4 per cent of the Earth's crust whereas gold makes up only a few millionths of 1 per cent. Naturally occurring alloys of elements, such as amalgams, are classified as elements in the mineral system.

21 Copper — Lake Superior (USA); actual size 10.5 cm

◁
20   Gold — Křepice, near Vodňany (Czech Republic); triangular crystals 5 mm in size (detail)

Copper - Cu

Cubic; H. 2.5-3; Sp. gr. 8.4-8.9 g/cm³; copper red; metallic lustre; S. reddish-brown

Copper was probably the first metal used by man. This is because copper ores are particularly abundant and the smelting of copper is comparatively easy. Ancient Rome gave copper the name *cuprum* (Cu) after Cyprus, where copper occurred. Copper is obtained chiefly from various ores in which it is usually present in compounds with other elements, though pure copper also sometimes does occur. Its crystals usually form distorted branching groups. Like most of the minerals which contain this metal, pure copper is generally conspicuously coloured on the surface. Most frequently it is covered with blue azurite and green malachite. The native metal occurs through the crystallisation of hot solutions, or through the decomposition of sulphur-containing copper ores in the surface layers of ore veins (called the cementation zone). The main sources of copper mining are in Michigan (USA), Australia, Cornwall (UK), and the Urals (Russia).

22   Silver — Kongsberg (Norway); actual size 9 cm

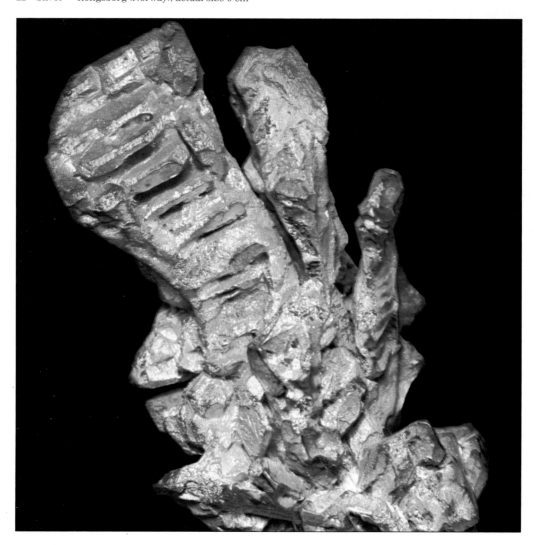

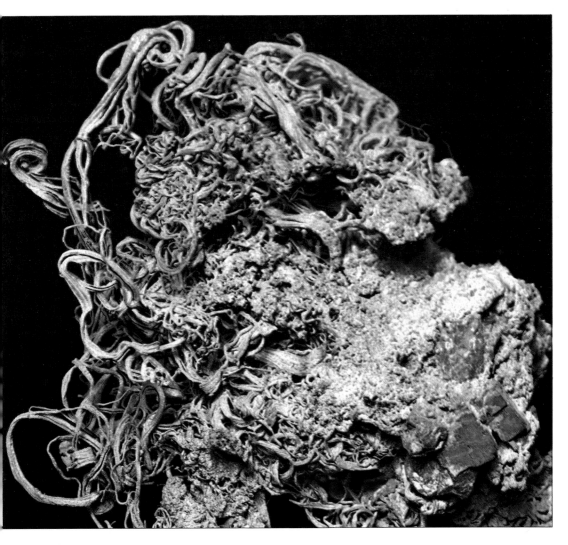

23   Silver — Příbram (Czech Republic); actual size 7 cm

Silver - Ag

Cubic; H. 2.5-3; Sp. gr. 9.6-12 g/cm³; silvery white, yellow on surface, with brown to black shades; strongly metallic lustre; S. silvery white

Silver, like copper, occurs not only in compounds but also as pure metal. It has been used through the ages. Archaeologists have found silver jewellery in the vaults of Chaldean kings from the 4th millennium BC. The oldest European silver mines were discovered in Spain where silver was extracted by the Phoenicians, Carthaginians and Moors. Saxony (Freiberg) and Bohemia were later centres of silver production; it is said that silver was mined there from the 7th century. After the discovery of America, the importation of silver from Mexico and Peru caused a slump in the European mining industry. Desire for silver was at one time as strong as desire for gold and, still in the 17th century, silver in Japan was actually priced the same as gold. Because of this, the countries that were rich in silver prospered during the days when large silver deposits were mined.

Pure silver usually occurs as distorted wires, often intertwined. Other irregular shapes such as plates, sheets, crusts and coatings, compact lumps and isometric crystals are less common. Silver usually occurs as the product of the decomposition of silver sulphide ores, for example galena and argentite, in the upper layers of the rock (it is called the oxidative and cementation zone). The chief European deposits today are at Kongsberg in Norway; non-European deposits are in Mexico and North America (Lake Superior) and Zmeinogorsk in the Altai (Russia). Some deposits, such as those in the vicinity of Schneeberg in Germany and in Peru, have yielded large boulders of silver, some of which weighed as much as several tonnes. In Jáchymov (Bohemia) where in the 16th century large quantities of silver were still being recovered from the rich surface veins, silver wires up to 30 cm in length were found. Similar finds have been made at Kongsberg in Norway. In the Saxony deposits, particularly in Freiberg, and at Schneeberg, it was common to find silver in fine bars, often more than 40 cm long. Freshly found pure silver has a magnificent silver colour and lustre. Both, however, quickly vanish when exposed to air; the silver blackens as it becomes coated with a layer of silver sulphide. Pure silver has a soft texture. Silver alloys containing other metals are therefore manufactured and are used mainly for coinage and in the jewellery industry, whereas in medicine and the photographic industry silver compounds are generally used.

Gold - Au

Cubic; H. 2.5-3; Sp. gr. 15.5-19.3 g/cm^3; golden yellow to whitish (when with a greater admixture of silver); metallic lustre; S. golden yellow to silver

Gold has always played a major role in history. Throughout the ages the very thought of gold created visions of riches and power. Alchemists therefore tried to manufacture gold from other substances, but without success. Archaeological evidence shows that gold was most probably the first metal man ever knew. Man looked for gold in the gravel and sand of rivers and centered all his strength and practical knowledge on recovering it. The first gold decorative objects which have been preserved come from the early Stone Age. The value of gold must have always been extremely high, for it was used in coinage from as early as the 7th century BC.

Gold is usually scattered so finely in rocks that it cannot be seen with the naked eye. Only rarely does it form larger soft plates, grains, or nuggets. The most beautiful gold plates were found in a boulder near Křepice in southern Bohemia. The largest nuggets come from deposits in America and Victoria (Australia), where, near Ballarat, a nugget weighing 85 kg was found in 1869; it was given the name 'Welcome Stranger'. If gold as such is a rarity, what a rare and exceptional find its perfectly bounded octahedral or cubic crystals must be. Gold does not oxidise and, in normal conditions, does not combine with other elements, so it is

24 Gold — Ballarat (Australia); actual size 6 cm

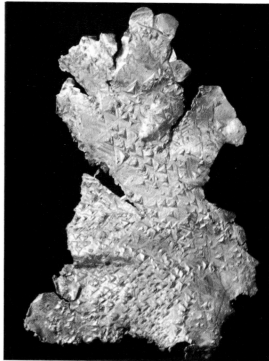

25 Gold — Rosia Montana (Romania); actual size of detail 5 cm

26 Gold — Křepice, near Vodňany (Czech Republic); triangular crystals 5 mm in size

usually found under natural conditions fairly pure, and only rarely as a compound. In the original rock it occurs either through deposition from hot water or through decomposition of gold-bearing sulphides, mainly pyrites and antimonite, in which traces of gold are often found.

Until recently, up to 50 per cent of the world's gold production came from the old deposits (gold-bearing conglomerates) in South Africa's Transvaal (Witwatersrand) and Orange Free State (Odendaalsrus). Other major deposits are in America (for example, Mother Lode in California), Canada and Siberia. In Europe there are deposits in France, Romania and Slovakia. Gold is suitable not only for the manufacture of jewels but is also used in medicine, coinage and the glass industry. Gold alloys are used in engineering (contacts, for example), and in dentistry.

The native alloy of pure gold and silver, which occurs in deposits of pure gold, is called electrum. It was named this because of its pale yellow colour (the Latin word *electrum* means 'amber').

Gold is perfectly malleable and ductile. It is possible to beat it into such a fine leaf (0.00014 mm thick) that it becomes transparent yellow-green; from 1 g of gold a wire of up to 160 m in length can be drawn. Only metals of the platinum group surpass the density of gold. However, gold is very soft and is therefore usually cast with harder metals such as copper, silver, platinum or nickel.

Platinum - Pt

Cubic; H. 1.5-2; Sp. gr. 14-19 g/cm³ (21 when pure); steel-silver colour; metallic lustre; S. grey

Platinum is one of the most important and valuable natural pure metals. But there were times when it was cheaper than silver, to which it is similar and for which it was originally mistaken. Platinum was found for the first time in the 16th century in deposits of gold in the alluvium of the Pinto river (today's San Juan) in Colombia. It did not catch the attention of scientists until 1748 when a Spanish traveller, Ulloa, told of the discovery of 'silver' which refused to melt.

Platinum usually occurs as grains and scales in alluvia where it has been carried from magmatic rocks with a small content of silicon dioxide. The largest deposits are near Sudbury in Ontario (Canada) and in the Urals. Smaller deposits occur in South Africa, in the USA and in the drainage basin of the San Juan river near Bogotá in Colombia. The chief use of platinum is in the manufacture of chemicals and jewellery. Platinum usage is constantly rising. Research has shown that platinum is the main representative of a group of metals with which it forms alloys under natural conditions. The metals of this group, including paladium, osmium, iridium and others, are very heavy and are used chiefly in electronic engineering, metallurgy and chemistry.

Like platinum itself, its compounds are very rarely found under natural conditions. Beautiful crystals of the very rare sperrylite (platinum arsenide, $PtAs_2$) have recently been found near Norilsk in northern Siberia.

27   Platinum — Nizhni Tagil, the Urals (Russia); actual size 5 cm, weight 84.8 g

28   Arsenic — Příbram (Czech Republic); actual height of detail 3 cm

Arsenic - As

Rhombohedral; H. 3; Sp. gr. 5.7 g/cm³; tin white, with dark shades; S. grey

Arsenic and its compounds have been known to be poisonous since ancient times; they were obtained from various minerals, mainly from arsenopyrite. As a pure element arsenic is comparatively rare. Its most common appearance is in round, irregular shell form with a smooth or indistinctly crystalline surface. It also occurs as a lump, fine-grained, kidney-shaped, rarely in the form of imperfect crystals. It is white in colour but soon turns darker on exposure. It occurs on silver and cobalt veins. The main deposits are at Freiberg (Saxony), Jáchymov (Czech Republic), Wittichen in the Black Forest (Germany), and in Japan and Chile.

At present, arsenic (especially arsenic extracted from its sulphide ores) is used in making medicaments, paints and pesticides (agriculture), for manufacturing glass and for impregnating wood.

A natural compound of arsenic and antimony, allemontite, forms kidney-shaped or cup-shaped stratified structures and is tin-white in colour. Like arsenic, allemontite occurs naturally in ore veins, but is comparatively rare; therefore it has no economic significance. Allemontite was discovered in 1822 by the French crystallographer, René Just Haüy (1743-1822).

Graphite - *carbon*, C

Hexagonal or rhombohedral; H. 1; Sp. gr. 2.1-2.3 g/cm³; iron black to steel grey; metallic lustre; S. black

Graphite has been used for decorating clay vessels. It has often been confused with similar minerals, especially molybdenite, and with antimony and lead ores. In the 18th century it was thought that graphite was a carbon with small amounts of iron. The name graphite comes from the Greek *graphein* (to write) and was introduced in 1789 by the German mineralogist, A. Werner. The Swedish chemist J. Berzelius (1779-1848) later discovered that graphite is pure carbon — hence, like diamond, graphite is one of the carbon modifications. The properties of the two minerals depend on the distribution of atoms in their structure. Carbon is commonly found in a scaly to massive form and develops usually through the metamorphism of coal, though it may also be of inorganic origin. Well-known graphite deposits are in the Bohemian Forest area (on both the Czech and Bavarian side) and the largest sources are located in Sri Lanka. Graphite was formerly used for the manufacture of pencils but today its main use is for making refractory crucibles, in steel smelting and in nuclear technology.

Lump graphite, called shungite, which is mined near Lake Ladoga in Russia, is used for making decorative objects.

29 Graphite — Sri Lanka; actual size of detail 5.5 cm

Diamond - *carbon, C*

Cubic; H. 10; Sp. gr. 3.52 g/cm³; clear, yellow, brown, green, less frequently blue to black; adamantine lustre

   Diamond is one of the most valuable precious stones and its unequalled physical properties place it in a unique position among other minerals. The discovery of diamonds dates back to ancient times. The Roman naturalist, Pliny the Elder (AD 23–79), wrote about diamonds, though Romans knew only diamonds of small dimensions. There are many traditional tales about the discovery and fate of old Indian diamonds, though the majority of the large diamonds of historical value were found only at the beginning of the 17th century. The nature of diamonds remained a mystery for a long time. The physicist Isaac Newton stated in 1675 that diamond was combustible; he came to this conclusion because of the diamond's exceptional ability to bend light rays. In 1694, the Italians Averani and Targioni carried out an experiment during which they burnt a diamond, using a glass lens. Sir Humphry Davy (1778–1829) later proved that diamond actually is carbon.

   Since olden days, diamonds have been found in the form of grains and small rounded octahedrons in alluvial deposits where they had been carried from dark igneous rocks. Efforts to find diamonds in their original rock hardly ever met with success. There are only four known instances of diamonds being found in their parent rock. The oldest one is the famous mine in the Kimberley region of South Africa, where they occur

30   Diamond in kimberlite — Kimberley (South Africa); actual size of crystal 1 x 1 cm

31 Cut diamonds — Kimberley (South Africa); actual size of the largest: 23.8 mm in diameter, weight 42.9 carat

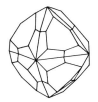

in decomposed peridotite known as kimberlite. Another substantial deposit of diamonds in parent rock is in the Viliuy river basin in Siberia. In 1961 diamonds in kimberlite were discovered in Sierra Leone (Africa) and lately also in India. Today the main African alluvial deposits are in Congo, Zaire, Angola, Tanzania, Ghana, Guinea, Ivory Coast and Liberia.

The most famous diamond fields where renowned large stones were found were in India. Valuable diamonds from local deposits usually became the property of the Indian princes, rajas and maharajas. They were kept in their treasures and passed from generation to generation. Others were placed among the treasures of various temples. These stones did not reach other countries, particularly Europe, until later, mostly as spoils of war. The first news of large Indian diamonds came to Europe from the French traveller Jean Baptiste Tavernier, who, in 1665, was commissioned to make a study of Indian treasures. The Republic of South Africa is the best known source of diamonds at the present time, though its output is not the greatest. The diamond fields of South Africa were not discovered until 1871. From the time of their discovery up to 1920 they produced more diamonds than all the mines of the rest of the world from ancient times.

The history of many of the diamond discoveries is interesting and the fate of the stones is vivid and dramatic. Precious diamonds for jewellery are today usually ground and polished to a brilliant cut of several facets. Diamonds which are very small and less valuable are ground to a rosette cut. Most people are unaware that only about 23 per cent of the diamonds found are suitable for precious gems and that the balance of production is used for industry. Diamonds for industrial use are, at the present time, also manufactured synthetically.

32 Diamond — Kimberley
(South Africa); actual size
of crystal 1.5 cm

Sulphur - S

Orthorhombic; H. 1.5-2; Sp. gr. 2.0-2.1 g/cm³; yellow to brown; adamantine to greasy lustre; S. colourless to yellow

There are many minerals which contain sulphur and they are mined at all sites where larger deposits occur. However, occasionally sulphur occurs also as a pure element and it was in this form that man first came across it. As it was of volcanic origin and burned with ease, ancient humans thought it had supernatural powers. In the past the Romans knew sulphur chiefly from the Sicilian deposits which even today have generous yields. It did not take long before they found various uses for sulphur, especially when they discovered the ease with which it burns with its intense blue flame, giving off sharp, irritating fumes which induce tears and coughing. During the 18th century many natural scientists pondered over the cause of sulphur's high burning capacity and they concluded that sulphur must be a mixture of vitriol and a special inflammable matter which they called 'phlogiston'. That sulphur is an element was discovered only in 1809, when scientific chemistry started developing.

Sulphur deposits are usually of volcanic origin. However, there are other known

33   Sulphur — Caltanissetta (Sicily); actual size of detail 11 x 9 cm

occurrences, caused by deposition from hot water and through the activity of certain organisms. Sulphur is also abundantly present in coal deposits, where it forms through sublimation during burning. Much sulphur also develops through the decomposition of some of the sulphur ores.

Sulphur crystals are usually in pyramidal form, sometimes tabular, usually grouped in druses. They occur in crevices of deposits and sometimes are as much as 10 cm in size. They have a strong diamond lustre and a conspicuous light yellow to honey yellow-brown colour. But the crystals are so fragile that they often crack on handling because of the warmth of the hand. Their weight is low and so is the degree of their hardness. The perfectly bounded faces of sulphur crystals are remarkable. Sulphur occurs even more frequently in the form of irregular masses or sheets, granular or star-shaped aggregates and impregnations. The aggregates often have a kidney-shaped surface and form tubers or stalactites and stalagmites. The sulphur coatings are usually earthy.

The 5 km wide belt between Mount Etna and Agrigento in Sicily is one of the richest sources of sulphur which, until recently, yielded almost a quarter of the world's sulphur supply. However, in the first half of the 20th century, mining in Sicily was exceeded by high North American production. Apart from Sicily, other large European sulphur deposits are in Poland in the Tarnobrzeg region. America (Louisiana and Texas with the Boling deposit) shares about 75 per cent of the world's sulphur reserves, which are estimated at 250 million tonnes. The deposits of pure sulphur are of importance because their recovery involves merely a cleaning process. Nevertheless, the biggest quantity of sulphur for commercial use is not extracted from such deposits but is manufactured by the roasting of pyrites.

Sulphur is used mainly for the production of sulphur oxides and sulphuric acid, which then serves as raw material for the manufacture of sulphur compounds, paints and medicaments. Much sulphur (in powder form) is used to destroy parasitic fungi and insects and also for the impregnation of wood, for the sulphuration of wooden barrels, for vulcanising rubber, for the manufacture of pulp and a variety of other products.

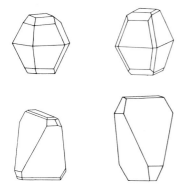

34 Sulphur — Caltanissetta (Sicily); actual size 7 x 4 cm

Chapter 2

SULPHIDES AND SIMILAR COMPOUNDS

This group comprises sulphides and similar compounds of arsenic, antimony, tellurium and selenium. They are included in the same group because arsenic, antimony, tellurium and selenium (whose occurrence is much less common), have similar properties and behaviour to sulphur. Sulphides are usually metallic, with only a few exceptions. They used to be divided into blendes, glances and pyrites. Blendes are non-metallic sulphides, glances and pyrites are metallic; glances are darker and of softer texture, pyrites are lighter in colour but harder. In the past sulphides were also divided into true sulphides, which had a simple chemical composition, and more complex sulpho-salts, containing, apart from sulphur and metal, other elements which behave like sulphur — for instance iron, cobalt, nickel, bismuth, arsenic or antimony. This form of classification is no longer used today. The current system proceeds from sulphides with a receding metal component to non-metallic sulphides. Sulpho-salts are, on the one hand, included among the sulphides of their respective structure types and, on the other hand, combined in so-called complex sulphides.

36   Hessite — Botes (Romania); actual size 10 cm

Hessite - *silver telluride*, Ag_2Te

Monoclinic; H. 2.5; Sp. gr. 8.31–8.45 g/cm³; lead to steel grey; metallic lustre; S. black

Hessite is one of the few natural tellurides. Its form is usually massive, or the crystals are many-sided, often distorted. It sometimes occurs in gold- or silver-bearing quartz veins. The main deposits are at Botes in Transylvania (Romania), the Zavadinsk mine in the Altay mountains of southern Russia, Calaveras in California and Coquimbo in Chile. Hessite is an uncommon ore of silver.

Of the remaining tellurides, two others are well worth mentioning: tellurobismuthite, telluride of bismuth, Bi_2Te_3, which occurs in faintly yellow, foliaceous to massive aggregates of gold-bearing quartz veins; and tetradymite, sulphotelluride of bismuth, Bi_2Te_2S. The latter was named after the Greek word *tetradymos* ('fourfold'), because the crystals found in some deposits were twinned on four sides. It is steel grey, has a perfect cleavage and conspicuous metallic lustre. On rare occasions it is found in association with gold in gold-bearing veins in young extrusive rocks and their tuffs (such as the andesite tuffs).

Berzelianite - *copper selenide*, Cu_2Se

Cubic; H. 2; Sp. gr. 6.71 g/cm³; grey-white; metallic lustre with blue to black shades; S. grey

Berzelianite, found in the copper ore mine at Akrikerum southwest of Stockholm, was first identified by the Swedish scientist Johan Berzelius in 1818. Like all selenides, berzelianite belongs among the very rare minerals — it occurs in only a few places in carbonate veins. However, about thirty years ago berzelianite was unexpectedly found at several sites at the Czech and Moravian border areas, and the deposits were comparatively large. The mineral forms fine-grained aggregates in calcite veins, together with other rare selenides. Like copper ores, berzelianite develops through crystallisation from hot solutions.

37 Berzelianite — Bukov (Czech Republic); actual height of detail 18 mm

Bornite - *sulphide of iron and copper*, Cu_3FeS_4

Cubic; H. 3; Sp. gr. 4.9–5.3 g/cm^3; copper red to bronze; metallic lustre; S. black

Chalcocite - *copper sulphide*, Cu_2S

Orthorhombic; H. 2.5–3; Sp. gr. 5.7–5.8 $g/cm;^3$; grey; metallic lustre; S. grey

Bornite and chalcocite usually occur in mixtures in common deposits. Both are classified as sulphides of metallic nature. They are usually found in the hydrothermal veins of copper ores, especially in the subsurface zone. Both are important copper ores.

Bornite is sometimes called 'variegated copper ore' because of its vivid shading. It is compact or granular, only occasionally crystallised. Its largest deposits are at Butte, Montana (USA), and in Mexico. European deposits are found near Salzburg (Austria) and Vrančice (Czech Republic). Crystalline bornite is found at Redruth in Cornwall (UK).

Chalcocite is more abundant than bornite. It also more often forms thick tabular or short columnar crystals. Finest specimens are found in the Anaconda mine at Butte, Montana, and in Redruth (crystals as large as 4.5 cm).

38   Chalcocite — Redruth (England); actual size of largest crystal 7 mm

Argentite - *silver sulphide*, Ag₂S

Cubic; H.2; Sp. gr. 7.3 g/cm³; black, with strong metallic lustre on fresh surfaces, commonly with dark hues and non-lustrous; S. grey to black

Argentite, or silver glance, was the principal silver ore of the Erzgebirge (Ore Mountains) on the Czech – German frontier during their reign of fame. Georgius Agricola, 'the father of mineralogy', wrote about argentite in 1529 and described it as a silver ore of lead colour, occurring in abundance in the mines of Jáchymov, Bohemia. He added that this mineral resembles galena (lead sulphide, PbS) and had not been known in ancient times. In 1598 the same ore was described by the famous Prague coiner, Lazar Ercker of Schreckenfels. During this era of tremendous mining development, substantial quantities of argentite were found below the surface in the Erzgebirge deposits and were responsible for the valuable silver recovered.

Argentite forms compact fillers of veins, or is of wiry shapes which represent pseudomorphs of native silver. It quickly loses its lustre and darkens on fresh surfaces — a trait by which it is distinguishable from galena. It can be cut with an ordinary knife. In contrast to galena, it has no cleavage but has a distinct hook-shaped fracture. It is also noted for its high density. It seldom crystallises, and then the crystals are distorted and imperfectly formed.

It is found in ore veins together with other silver ores, especially with the silver-bearing galenite. The most important European deposits are at Freiberg and Schneeberg in Saxony, Banská Štiavnica in Slovakia, and outside Europe in the Comstock Lode in Nevada (USA) and near Guanajuato, northwest of Mexico City. Some of these

deposits, such as the ones in Saxony, have yielded boulders of argentite up to 4 kg in weight, or large interwoven and net-like aggregates. In the Comstock Lode it occurs in large compact clusters and in abundant quantities with other noble silver ores (ores containing silver in their formula). Argentite is, after native silver, the richest silver ore with a metal content of more than 87 per cent.

39 Argentite — Jáchymov (Czech Republic); actual size of crystals 4 mm

40   Sphalerite — Banská Štiavnica (Slovakia); actual size of crystals 1 cm

Sphalerite - *zinc sulphide*, ZnS

Cubic; H. 3–4; Sp. gr. 3.5–4.2 g/cm³; brown to black, less frequently yellow, greenish to red, rarely colourless (cleiophane); greasy to adamantine lustre; S. yellow to brown

Sphalerite derives its name from the Greek *sphaleros* ('deceitful', 'uncertain'). This is because it occurs in such varied colours that even expert miners often failed to recognise it. Even in the 16th century they still mistook it for silver ore; only in the first half of the 18th century was it discovered that sphalerite contains a significant amount of zinc. It was, however, not used for practical purposes till the 1860s, when a metallurgical method for extracting zinc from sphalerite was worked out. Until then it had been thrown away as useless gangue, especially as it was considered an unwelcome impurity in lead ores which caused difficulties in their metallurgical processing. Sphalerite is usually granular; on crevices it forms crystals of perfect cleavage and of strong metallic lustre. It is one of the most common sulphides and occurs in ore veins, usually with galena and pyrite, and sometimes chalcopyrite (polymetallic ores). The largest sphalerite deposits are in the regions of the upper Mississippi in the USA, and in Europe on the border of Germany and Belgium. Other important deposits are at Bleiberg in Carinthia (Austria), Příbram (Czech Republic) and Bytom in Polish Silesia. Magnificent specimens of yellow crystals have been found in north–western Spain in the Picos de Europa. That particular sphalerite is ground as a precious stone. Sphalerite is the main ore of zinc, which is used mainly for metal sheets and coatings resistant to oxidation. Gallium, indium and germanium, having semiconductor properties, are present as impurities in sphalerite and are recovered from it.

Wurtzite has the same chemical composition as sphalerite but differs in its internal structure and therefore also in the shape of its crystals (which are hexagonal). Unlike sphalerite it is comparatively rare; usually it is brown to yellow-brown, kidney-shaped or cup-shaped, radially acicular. It is found in association with sphalerite and galena in polymetallic ore veins.

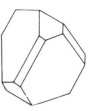

41 Chalcopyrite
— Baia Sprie
(Romania); actual
size 8 x 7 cm

Chalcopyrite - *sulphide of copper and iron*, $CuFeS_2$

Tetragonal; H. 3–4; Sp. gr. 4.1–4.3 g/cm^3; brass to goldish yellow; metallic lustre; S. grey-green

Chalcopyrite was well-known in the past to miners, because they could not help but notice its vivid surface colouring which is typical of several copper ores. These colours, chiefly mauve, blue and reddish, originate from the refraction of light beams in the weathered surface layer of the mineral. The true colour of chalcopyrite, not affected by weathering, is similar to the colour of pyrite, but it is richer, brassy to golden yellow, and usually bears a greenish tint. The identification of these two minerals is therefore simplified when the variability of their hues, crystal forms or the degree of hardness are considered. Chalcopyrite, unlike pyrite, can be scratched with a knife.

Chalcopyrite usually forms granular to compact fillers of veins; chalcopyrite crystals are rare. It occurs most frequently in ore veins, usually with other sulphides. The best known deposits are in the Alps (Mitterberg near Salzburg, Austria), Mannsfeld (the so-called 'copper slates') and Siegerland (beautiful crystals in the Clara mine) in Germany, Cornwall in the UK and Pennsylvania (USA). Chalcopyrite is the most widespread copper ore found under natural conditions; its copper content is almost 35 per cent.

Tetrahedrites - *group of minerals, complex sulphides of antimony, arsenic and copper*

Cubic; H. 3-4.5; Sp. gr. 4.4-5.1 g/cm^3; black to grey; metallic lustre, greasy on fresh fracture; S. grey, with metalloidal varieties also red to cherry red

Tetrahedrites are so named because they usually crystallise in tetrahedral form. However, tetrahedrite crystals do not occur very frequently, because these minerals are more often found as lump, coarse-grained, fine-grained or compact masses and their fracture is conchoidal or uneven. 'Tetrahedrites' is actually a collective name for a whole group of minerals which often intermingle in a most varied way. Because of this, some of them have been named as separate minerals. Tennantite, thus named in honour of the British chemist, Smithson Tennant (1761–1815), is composed mainly of arsenic; schwazite contains a substantial part of zinc, and the Saxon freibergite has a 30 per cent silver content. The tetrahedrites containing arsenic are light in colour (white-grey), whereas those with antimony are darker (almost black). Tetrahedrites occur in veins, usually with other minerals, such as chalcopyrite, bornite and other sulphides, especially pyrite, sphalerite, galena and argentite; sometimes they occur in cavities with native wire silver. On rare occasions tetrahedrites are found on contact deposits and in copper slates.

There are large tetrahedrite deposits in the Alps, in Romania, near Freiberg in Saxony, and in the Slovakian Erzgebirge (Ore Mountains). Rich druses of beautiful crystals occur mainly in Austria (Brixleg and Schwaz in Tirol), in Romania (Botes and Cavnic), United Kingdom (Cornwall), Algeria (containing silver) and the USA (Idaho).

Tetrahedrite is often mined not only as a rich copper ore (30–50 per cent copper) but also as a silver or mercury ore, or as an ore of other elements. These admixtures are recovered from the tetrahedrites as by-products.

42   Tetrahedrite — Cavnic (Romania); actual size of crystals 8.5 mm

Pyrrhotite (pyrrhotine) - *iron sulphide*, Fe_7S_8

Hexagonal; H. 4; Sp. gr. 4.6 g/cm³; yellow-brown to bronze yellow; metallic lustre; S. black

Pyrrhotite, or magnetopyrite, was given its name because, although similar to pyrite or marcasite, it is usually fairly strongly magnetic (when chemically pure and not accompanied by larger amounts of other minerals). Generally, it is finely granular or massive; only infrequently does it form hexagonal crystal plates. Its fracture is yellow-white in colour, but darkens very quickly. It occurs chiefly in some magmatic rocks and in crystalline schists. It is found either as huge deposits of finely granular pyrrhotite or as a fine cover of scattered grains. Another mode of origin is from solutions in ore veins when it develops in association with other sulphides, or from pyrite from the contact effects of igneous rocks. The largest deposits of pyrrhotite are at Sudbury, Ontario (Canada). Some magnificent crystal specimens have been found in Austria (Carinthia), Romania (Herja), France, Brazil, and recently mainly in the region around Norilsk in northern Siberia. Pyrrhotite is used for the manufacture of sulphur and sulphur compounds. Some types of pyrrhotite contain significant amounts of other elements, for example nickel and cobalt, and also gold and platinum. Such pyrrhotites are important ores of these metals, especially in the Urals (Russia) and at Sudbury, Ontario. The Sudbury pyrrhotite, containing nickel and some iron, is the most important nickel ore and is called pentlandite.

Niccolite, hexagonal nickel arsenide (NiAs), is another important nickel ore. Its colour is similar to that of pyrrhotite.

43   Pyrrhotite — Chiusbaia (Romania); actual size of crystals up to 4 cm

44   Millerite — Rapice, near Kladno (Czech Republic); actual size of needles up to 2 cm

Millerite - *nickel sulphide*, NiS

Rhombohedral; H. 3; Sp. gr. 5.3 g/cm³; brassy yellow to green-grey; metallic lustre; S. black

Millerite has been found in cavities in coal seams by miners in the Kladno region of central Bohemia for more than a hundred years. It forms fine hair-like crystals, consisting of flexible needles, brassy yellow in colour. These needles sometimes reach a remarkable length (6 cm) and miners call them 'golden hair'. The most magnificent examples can today be found in cracks of clayey siderites called pelosiderites, forming spherical structures. The millerite needles can be seen only after the ball-shaped formations are broken up. Millerite also occurs as a rare mineral in other places, for example in the Rhineland (Oberlara — crystals up to 7 cm in size), in Saxony (Freiberg, Johanngeorgenstadt), in Canada and some states of the USA. Specimens found in limestone cavities near St. Louis, Missouri, are particularly magnificent. Though the nickel content is nearly 56 per cent, it is never considered as a nickel ore. This is because nowhere in the world does it occur in workable quantities.

45 Galena — Freiberg, Saxony (Germany); actual size of crystals 2 cm

Galena - *lead sulphide*, PbS

Cubic; H. 2.5–3; Sp. gr. 7.2–7.6 g/cm³; grey-black to lead grey; very strong metallic lustre; S. grey

Galena has been recovered since ancient times and it is mentioned by writers of that period. It is known that lead was obtained from galena in those times because the process of extracting it was very easy. The Babylonians made lead vases and the Romans used lead to make water pipes. After the invention of letterpress printing, lead began to be extensively used as the basis of type metal.

Galena is a common mineral of ore veins of various compositions. It occurs in conspicuously granular form or as cubic crystals. It has a perfect cleavage, and often crumbles readily into small cubes when struck. It is rather heavy. The largest galena deposits are in the valleys of the Missouri and Mississippi in the USA and in Europe at Bleiberg in Carinthia (Austria) and at Bytom in Upper Silesia (Poland). Galena is also mined at Příbram and Stříbro (Czech Republic). The largest galena crystals, up to 25 cm in size, have been found in the Isle of Man (UK). Galena is the most important ore of lead, of which it contains nearly 87 per cent. Apart from the manufacture of type metal, lead today is principally used for cable covering, accumulator plates and as shielding for radioactive substances. Its compounds are used for the manufacture of paints, particularly white and red, and also for lead glass and enamel. Because of its widespread occurrence, galena is also the most common ore of silver, though its silver content is not greater than 0.5 per cent.

52

Cinnabar - *mercury sulphide*, HgS

Rhombohedral - pseudocubic; H. 2–2.5; Sp. gr. 8.2 g/cm³; reddish; adamantine to metallic lustre; S. red

Cinnabar was recovered by ancient Greeks as early as the 7th century BC in southern Spain, especially around Almadén. In those days they used it mainly as a red pigment and called it *kinnabari* (this gave the mineral its name). But the Romans found it was a source of 'quicksilver' (mercury). They learned how to make an excellent black paint from it. Cinnabar, therefore, was an important mineral. The alchemists of the Middle Ages believed that gold could be recovered from it.

Cinnabar forms finely grained to compact, massive or earthy aggregates and crusts, and sometimes crystals. It occurs most frequently in separate ore veins. Apart from Almadén, which even today is one of the largest sources of mercury in the world, there are other well-known sources in Tuscany (Italy), at Avala near Belgrade (Serbia), and in California (USA). The largest crystals of cinnabar were found in the Chinese province of Hu-nan; crystals and beautiful twins up to 4.5 cm in size are found in the Wan-shan-khang deposit. Cinnabar is the chief ore of mercury, of which it contains 86 per cent. Mercury is very important in medicine and in the manufacture of ammunition. Less significant today is its use for working valuable metals, particularly in the extraction of silver and gold from ores and in the manufacture of paints. It is worth noting that the consumption of mercury has not risen during the last few decades, for in some instances, such as in the manufacture of mirrors, less expensive substances are used.

46   Cinnabar — Almadén (Spain); actual size of crystals up to 2 cm

Antimonite (stibnite) - *antimony sulphide*, Sb_2S_3

Orthorhombic; H. 2–2.5; Sp. gr. 4.63 g/cm³; lead to steel grey with rainbow shade; metallic lustre; S. grey

Antimonite was known to the Roman natural scientist, Pliny, who mentioned it in his writings as a cosmetic preparation of that time: the silver grey antimonite was finely ground to be used for colouring the eyelids. Antimonite occurs in various veins together with other ores, or in veins which are often gold-bearing. It forms elongated crystals which may be of hair-like shape. It is sometimes found in masses. It is well known for its strikingly beautiful crystals which were found in the Japanese island of Shikoku and were used as ornaments. The mining in Japan has long since ceased and the crystals, which sometimes measured as much as 1 m, are today a precious rarity. They were most popular with the local inhabitants, who used them as flower supports or to make the little fences of Japanese miniature gardens. These unusual crystal creations of the mineral kingdom often also formed an essential part of the interior decor of many dwellings. The strange beauty of the Japanese antimonite vein cavities was exceptional. The walls of these natural caves were garnished with rich druses and tufts of the most magnificent columnar crystals, as dazzling as polished steel. Today they can be seen only in museum collections.

47   Antimonite — Cavnic (Romania); actual size of crystals up to 4 cm

The largest deposits of antimonite are in Mexico and in the Jiangxi province in China. The richest European deposits are at Bohutín and at Milešov near Příbram (Czech Republic), in the Little Carpathians (Slovakia), in Sardinia and Tuscany (Italy) and near Fojnica, Krupanj and Kostajnik (Serbia). Beautiful druses of antimony are found in Romania (Baia Sprie and Chiusbaia). Antimonite is the chief ore of antimony, of which it contains up to 71 per cent. Nearly three-quarters of the production is used for the manufacture of various alloys, particularly type metal (alloy of antimony and lead).

Berthierite - *sulphide of iron and antimony*, $FeSb_2S_4$

Orthorhombic, H. 2–3; S.gr. 4.6 g/cm³; dark steel grey with bronze shade; metallic lustre; S. dark grey

Berthierite is so named in honour of P. Berthier (1782–1861) and is not a particularly well-known mineral. It usually forms needle-shaped to compact aggregates which resemble antimonite. The difference appears in berthierite's colour, which is dark steel grey with a vivid bronze-brown streak. It occurs in ore veins, mainly with antimonite. The chief deposits are: Freiberg (Saxony), Bohutín near Příbram (Czech Republic), Baia Sprie and Chiusbaia (Romania), and Oruro (Bolivia).

Rather similar chemical composition is shared by miargyrite, (sulphide of silver and antimony, $Ag_2Sb_2S_4$). This was named after the Greek *meion* ('less') and *argyrion* ('silver'), because it contained less silver than other similar silver ores with which it was

48   Berthierite — Herja (Romania); actual size of detail 9 x 6 cm

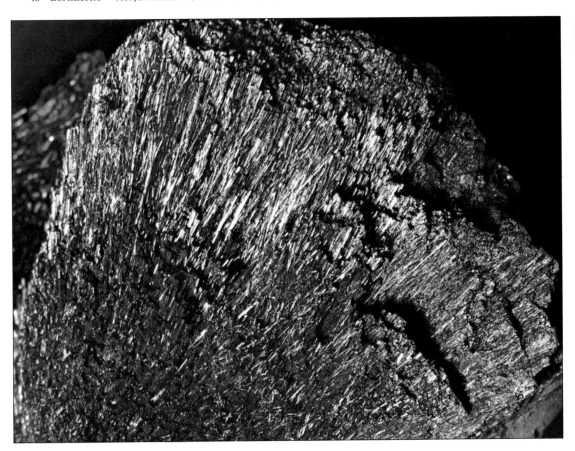

frequently associated. It occurs in the form of monoclinic minute multi-faced crystals of tabular or other shapes, and in compact or granular aggregates. When fresh, it is dark red, like pyrargyrite, but through weathering it becomes tainted grey to almost black. Miargyrite appears comparatively rarely in hydrothermal veins of silver ore, chiefly in Zacatecas, Mexico, in Braunsdorf, Saxony, and at Příbram, Czech Republic.

Bournonite - *sulphide of lead, copper and antimony*, $PbCuSbS_3$

Orthorhombic; H. 2.5–3; Sp. gr. 5.7–5.9 g/cm³; dark grey; metallic lustre; S. steel grey to blackish

 Bournonite was found long ago in the cavities of ore veins in the Harz mountains (Germany), which are rich in ores. It also occurred at Příbram, Czech Republic, and in Cornwall, Great Britain, where it was present in large quantities around Endellion, and was recovered as a good antimony ore. (The mineral was also known in Britain as endellionite). Several deposits of bournonite also exist in Carinthia, Austria. The name bournonite was given to the mineral in honour of the French crystallographer and mineralogist who described its chemical composition. The crystals of bournonite are mostly tabular with square contours. Sometimes they are intergrown and form interprenetrant twins. The occurrence of low columnar crystals is less common. Bournonite is also found fairly frequently in the form of well developed crystals in ore veins, or it is massive, granular to compact, recognisable by its strong lustre. It is comparatively fragile. Bournonite is used as an ore of lead, copper and antimony.

49 Bournonite — Hornhausen (Germany); actual size of crystals up to 1 cm

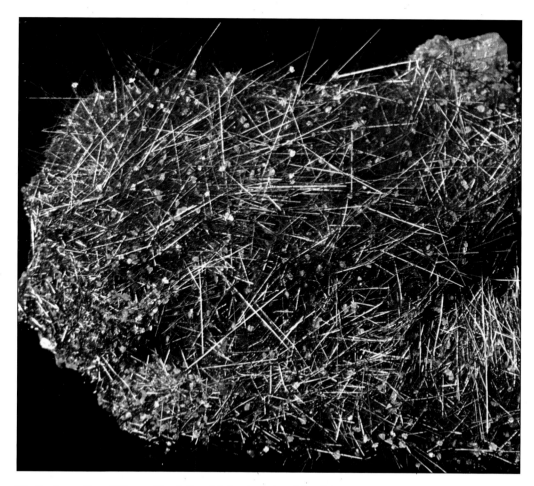

50   Boulangerite — Příbram (Czech Republic); actual size of detail 8 x 6 cm

Boulangerite - *sulphide of lead and antimony,* $Pb_5Sb_4S_{11}$

Orthorhombic; H. 2.5; Sp.gr. 5.8–6.2 g/cm³; bluish lead grey to iron black; metallic lustre; S. brown-grey to brown

Boulangerite was named after the French mining engineer, C. L. Boulanger (1810–1849). Owing to its very unusual appearance, it is one of the most interesting and sought-after minerals. It is usually finely fibrous, while the individual fibres are long, needle-like crystals, grouped into interpenetrant fibrous aggregates. This is why it is often called, together with other rare sulphides, 'felt-like ore'. Boulangerite occurs in hydrothermal ore veins with other sulphides (polymetallic veins). The main deposits are Mollières (France), Wolfsberg in the Harz mountains, Příbram (Czech Republic), places in Upper Silesia (Poland), and Nerchinsk in the Urals (Russia). Boulangerite is an ore of lead with 55.2 per cent metal.

Another mineral of the group of felt-like ores is jamesonite, named after the mineralogist Robert James (1774–1854). It forms monoclinic, finely fibrous dark grey small crystals similar to those of boulangerite, which are also grouped mostly in felt-like aggregates. It is found on hydrothermal beds and in veins of gold-bearing quartz. Its main deposits are Arnsberg in Westphalia, Wolfsberg in the Harz mountains and Freiberg in Saxony (Germany). Other deposits are at Kasejovice and Příbram (Czech Republic) and Zlatá Ida and Nižná Slaná near Košice (Slovakia). Needles up to 20 cm long have been found at the last-mentioned site.

Proustite - *sulphide of arsenic and silver*, Ag_3AsC_3

Rhombohedral; H. 2.5; Sp. gr. 5.57 g/cm³; grey-red, turning grey to black in light; adamantine lustre; S. lightly scarlet

Proustite is among the so-called 'noble ores' of silver. In the past the adjective 'noble' was given to ores with a high content of silver. Proustite was known even then because it was so conspicuous with its scarlet colour and high lustre. When exposed to light, however, proustite soon loses the lustre and turns grey, almost black. This happens through the formation of a thin layer of metallic silver on the surface (a similar photochemical reaction as on a photographic plate). Proustite is usually granular and sometimes massive, but the crystallised form is less common. It occurs in ore veins, mainly in deposits of arsenic ores. Some spectacular columnar crystals come from Saxony in Germany (Freiberg, Annaberg), from Jáchymov (Czech Republic), from the Mexican state of Chihuahua, and especially from Chile — crystals up to 5 cm in size occur in the Chanarcillo deposit in Chile. Proustite is one of the most important silver ores and it contains as much as 65.4 per cent of the metal.

Pyrargyrite is very like proustite, but instead of arsenic it contains antimony. When fresh, pyrargyrite is, in contrast to proustite, of a dark red colour, with a metallic to

51 Proustite —
Chaňarcillo (Chile);
actual size 7 cm

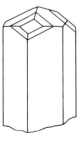

52   Pyrite — Utah (USA); actual size 4 x 4 cm

diamond lustre. When exposed to light it acquires the same hues as proustite. It also forms columnar crystals, but more frequently massive, granular, or compact aggregates.

Pyrite - *iron disulphide*, FeS_2

Cubic; H. 6–6.5; S. gr. 4.9–5.2 g/cm^3; brassy yellow with greyish shadow to golden yellow, brownish, vividly shaded; metallic lustre; S. black with a brown hue

Pyrite was known even in ancient times. Its name is derived from the Greek *pyr* ('fire'), because sparks fly from it while it is being broken. In Greece it was considered to have healing powers (stopping 'blood decay') and was therefore worn as an amulet. The Incas in South America made mirrors from pyrite. Large polished slabs of pyrite

53   Pyrite — Rio Marina, Elba (Italy); actual size of detail 5.5 x 5.5 cm

have been found in their graves and this is why it is sometimes called 'the stone of the Incas'. Some practical facts relating to pyrite were compiled by natural scientists of the Middle Ages, who based their findings on the experience of miners. Many people are familiar with the small golden yellow grains or crystals of pyrite in coal, which at first glance look like gold. The black streak of pyrite (in contrast to the yellow streak of gold) soon proves the difference. The largest quantities of pyrite are contained in meta-morphosed and non-metamorphosed sedimentary rocks, in which pyrite develops by sedimentation in a poor supply of oxygen. Pyrite often forms crystals of various shapes and combinations. The typical shapes that are formed include cubes (often striated), octahedrons and pyritohedrons.

Even more commonly, pyrite occurs granular and massive. Its brassy yellow to gold-en yellow surface is often vividly tainted, usually blue, green or red. This is because it oxidises and weathers very quickly — particularly on the surface. It is advisable to take great care of any pyrite specimens in the collection, for as it decomposes it yields sul-phuric acid, which damages everything near it. Such alterations of course happen also under natural conditions, in which pyrite oxidises easily, and during this process various sulphates develop, such as gypsum, aluminite (hydrous alkaline aluminium sulphate), alum (hydrous double sulphates) and melanterite; other products of oxida-tion include hydrous ferric oxides, limonite and goethite. Pyrite decomposes easily in nitric acid and fuses readily. Its chemical properties make it an unwelcome component

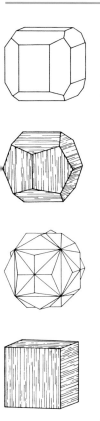

54 Pyrite —
Navajum (Spain);
actual size of
crystals 2 cm

of rocks used for the exterior decoration of buildings, for its presence soon causes unattractive rust-like stains and lines to form.

Río Tinto in Spain is an important production centre of pyrite, and so is Japan. Famous crystals come from the island of Elba, as well as from other Italian deposits such as at Gavorrano, and the Greek deposits of Khalkidiki and especially Xánthi, where crystals up to 0.5 m in size have been found. Crystallised pyrite also occurs in Sweden (Gällivare) and in Utah, USA. As a raw material, pyrite has many technical uses. Its chief use is for the production of sulphuric acid, sulphates, paints and polishes. It is usually processed by roasting. The by-products can be utilised as low-quality iron ore. An interesting feature of pyrite is that when ground for ornamental purposes, its lustre becomes quite exceptional. Some pyrites carry gold and copper and are therefore used as ores of these metals. The importance of pyrite as raw material for furnishing sulphur has diminished in recent decades following the mining of pure natural sulphur in newly discovered deposits and the utilisation of industrial gases with a sulphur content derived from coal.

Marcasite - *iron disulphide*, FeS_2

Orthorhombic; H. 5–6; Sp. gr. 4.6–4.9 g/cm³; pale bronze yellow; metallic lustre; S. black with brown shade, paler than that of pyrite

Marcasite is of the same chemical composition as pyrite. The colouring and a number of other properties are almost identical, so it is not surprising that the Greek word *pyrítés* ('of fire') was, in ancient times, given to marcasite as well as pyrite and that they were both regarded as healing stones right up to the Middle Ages. The French mineralogist René Just Haüy, was the first to distinguish (in 1814) between pyrite and marcasite. Today there are various tests to differentiate the two minerals.

Marcasite does not have the same internal structure as pyrite. Its crystals are usually small, flat-columnar. They are often twinned in unusual, very complex units. The crystals of the so-called 'spear pyrites' are cyclic 'quins', consisting of short-columnar, elongated crystals. These are of even more complicated form when thin crystals grow in parallel, one above the other. Parallel intergrowth of many twins is called 'cockscomb pyrite'. The aggregates are often compact, granular, acicular or radial with a reniform surface; there may also be stalactitic aggregates, or just very fine crusts. In coal

55 Marcasite — Komořany, near Most (Czech Republic); actual size 7 x 5.5 cm

cracks marcasite may occur in layers with a reniform surface and is then called 'liver pyrite'. The finely radiating aggregates in coal or the radiating concretions are often referred to by miners as 'oranges'. The variability in shape of marcasite is indeed immense. The colour of marcasite is almost identical to pyrite. It is also bronze-yellow, but slightly paler, with a greyish-green tint. It can be almost impossible to tell these two minerals apart by their colour alone.

Marcasite and pyrite are both found jointly in coal deposits and in metamorphic and non-metamorphic sedimentary rocks. Even their actual origin has similarities. However, marcasite is not so abundant under natural conditions. It occurs in concretions embedded

56 Marcasite — Sparta, Illinois (USA); actual size 6 cm

in clays and limestones, and less commonly it is present in some ore veins. Small quantities of marcasite appear in many places. It is present only in the surface layers of the Earth's crust because, in contrast to pyrite, it is deposited at low temperatures from acid solutions, or develops during the decomposition of plant or animal bodies.

If marcasite is placed inside a box, it will turn, after a while, into greyish dust and leave a stain smelling of sulphuric acid. This happens because marcasite oxidises even more readily than pyrite. The products of its decomposition are similar. Most frequently it alters into sulphates, particularly gypsum and limonite.

Folkestone and Dover in the UK have well-known marcasite deposits, famous for the chalk spear pyrites. There are large deposits at Freiberg in Saxony. Marcasite is also abundant in the lignite basins in the foothill area of the Erzgebirge in the Czech Republic, particularly around Sokolov. Embedded in coal, marcasite forms beautiful crystals of either cockscomb pyrite or spear pyrite form. Crusts of druses and kidney forms also occur. These are sometimes covered with tiny pyrite crystal cubes. Unfortunately, these marcasites are particularly unstable and are prone to swift decomposition and disintegration.

Only a few of the deposits are of commercial importance for mining marcasite as a raw material for the manufacture of sulphuric acid.

57 Arsenopyrite — Lingau (Austria); actual size 6.5 x 5 cm

Arsenopyrite - *sulphide of iron and arsenic*, FeAsS

Monoclinic, pseudorhombic; H. 5.5; Sp. gr. 6.07–6.15 g/cm³; grey to tin white, often with shadows; metallic lustre; S. dark grey-black

Arsenopyrite was first described in 1546 by Georgius Agricola, who called it 'the poisonous pyrite'. The ancient miners had known of its existence, but were unable to discern the subtle differences between arsenopyrite and several other pyrites of pale bronze colour. Scientists did not pay much attention to arsenopyrite until the end of the 18th century, and its chemical composition was not ascertained until 1812. The most famous deposits of arsenopyrite were at that time on the Czech side of the Riesengebirge (Giant Mountains). Arsenopyrite is a typical vein mineral, which occurs either with other sulphur ores (polymetallic veins), or individually. In appearance it somewhat resembles pyrite, for it also has yellowish hues. In fresh state its natural colour is tin white to steel grey. It is found in compact or crystal form. The largest arsenopyrite deposits are in Sweden, in the Aude département in France, near Freiberg in Saxony, in some localities around Salzburg (Austria) and in Mexico. Though the proportion of arsenic in arsenopyrite is large (up to 46 per cent), as much as 90 per cent of this element is obtained today from the arsenic impurities in other ores.

Molybdenite - *molybdenum sulphide*, MoS_2

Hexagonal; H. 1–1.5; Sp. gr. 4.7–4.8 g/cm³; lead grey; metallic lustre; S. green-grey

Molybdenite got its name by mistake: the Greek word *molybdos* means 'lead', for which it was mistaken. Molybdenite has a blue to violet hue and a metallic lustre. In ancient Greece, the word *molybdaina* was used not only for molybdenite but also for other similar minerals, such as some minerals with antimony, which were used for writing implements. In 1778, the Swedish chemist Carl Wilhelm Scheele took molybdenite out of this group of minerals. Molybdenite forms flexible hexagonal scales and leaflets of perfect cleavage, which often closely resemble graphite. It occurs mainly in granites and pegmatites which are hydrothermally metamorphosed, usually accompanied by cassiterite and wolframite. Nearly 90 per cent of the world's production of molybdenite comes from the deposits in Climax, Colorado. Other important deposits are in Chile. In Europe it occurs in Montenegro (in former Yugoslavia) and in the Czech Republic. Molybdenite is the most important ore of molybdenum, of which it contains 60 per cent and which is used in the manufacture of steel. It is also used as a solid lubricant.

58 Molybdenite — Krupka (Czech Republic); actual size 4 x 2.5 cm

Realgar - *arsenic sulphide*, AsS

Monoclinic; H. 1.5; Sp. gr. 3.5–3.6 g/cm³; orange-red to dark orange; greasy-vitreous to adamantine lustre; S. slightly paler than the surface colouring

Realgar is one of the natural arsenic compounds which were once used as paints. It was sold under various names — arsenic ruby, arsenic blende, or arsenic glass. Realgar originates through the decomposition of arsenic minerals, chiefly arsenopyrite, in ore veins. It forms grains or crystals. The most beautiful specimens come from Allchar north-west of Thessaloníki in Greece. There it occurs jointly with orpiment in rich deposits of arsenic ores. In a mixture of these two minerals one may occasionally find a bunch of slender columns of antimonite not yet decomposed — a primary antimony ore in this deposit. The specimens from Allchar are among the most colourful examples of various mineralogical groupings, for the contrast of golden yellow, blood red and deep steel blue-grey is extremely striking. Similar deposits are in Cavnic and Baia Sprie in Romania. The Gechtel mine in Humboldt county in Nevada is now the principal non-European deposit. Large columnar crystals of realgar are found there. Crystals up to 1.5 cm in size have been found in the Luchumi deposits in the Caucasus. The primary use of realgar today is in pyrotechnics for the preparation of the so-called 'White Flames of Greece' and in the tanning industry. As an arsenic ore it contains up to 70 per cent arsenic.

59　Realgar — Baia Sprie (Romania); actual size of largest crystal 6 mm

60 Orpiment with realgar — Baia Sprie (Romania); actual size 10 x 8 cm

61 Orpiment — Allchar (Greece); actual size 10 cm

Orpiment - *arsenic trisulphide*, As_2S_3

Monoclinic-pseudorhombic; H. 1.5–2; Sp. gr. 3.48 g/cm^3; golden yellow, brownish; greasy to pearly lustre; S. colourless

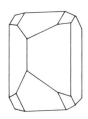

Orpiment, whose name means 'golden pigment', has been used for painting. Once it was exported from the Middle East to Europe in the form of large leaves up to 10 cm long under the name 'Turkish orpiment'. It came from Djulamerk in the land of the Kurds in southeastern Turkey near the Iraqi border. The natural deposits of orpiment are not sufficient to meet the substantial demand for the manufacture of paints, so it is also produced artificially under the name of 'king's yellow'. In some deposits orpiment accompanies other arsenic ores. It forms through the weathering of these ores and covers them in a yellow crust. In cavities it forms compact, cup-shaped, lamellar, reniform to globose nodules, with a radial arrangement inside. Crystals are rare. The main deposits are at Cavnic and Baia Sprie in Romania, Allchar in Greece and, as mentioned, Djulamerk. Crystals up to 60 cm in size are found in the Minkiule deposits in Yakutskaya in eastern Siberia. Orpiment is used as an arsenic ore and contains up to 61 per cent arsenic.

62   Halite — Salzkammergut (Austria); actual size of largest crystal 2.1 cm

Chapter 3   HALIDES

Halides are compounds of the so-called halogen elements, including chlorine, fluorine, bromine and iodine. Of these elements, the characteristics of fluorine are basically different from those of the other three. Minerals containing fluorine occur therefore in mineral parageneses entirely different from minerals with a content of chlorine, bromine and iodine. The most significant occurrences of fluorine-containing minerals are in granite rocks. The melanochroid magmas (high in silicon dioxide) and their exhalation products are poorer in fluorine but richer in chlorine. This is why active volcanoes with a predominance of melanochroid lavas show only traces of fluorine, but have a large quantity of chlorine. Chlorine, bromine and iodine are, however, amassed in inorganic sediments, particularly in the sedimentations from sea waters.

   Halides are rather poorly represented in the mineral kingdom in comparison with other groups of minerals. Only fluorite and common rock salt (halite) are plentiful.

Halite (common rock salt) - *sodium chloride*, NaCl

Cubic; H. 2; Sp. gr. 3.1–3.2 g/cm^2; colourless, grey, rarely reddish or blue; vitreous to dull lustre; S. colourless

   Common rock salt, or cooking salt, was an important object of trade in ancient times: it was supplied inland from maritime regions. It was, without doubt, human-kind's most essential mineral and today it remains one of our primary needs. Common salt is mentioned in the works of many ancient natural historians and philosophers. Pliny the Elder (AD 23–79), who was killed during an eruption of Vesuvius, listed various methods for recovering common salt from sea water or salt springs by evaporation. On the Mediterranean coast there were deposits of rock salt in Spain in the neighbourhood of Barcelona (Cardona). Rock salt was extracted from vast mines in India during the time of Alexander the Great (356–323 BC).

   Mining in the Austrian Salt Chamber dates back even further, for archaeological ex-cavations have proved that rock salt was mined there as long ago as the 15th century BC. The remains of ancient mines have been discovered near Hallstatt and, apart from the underground tunnels and passages, the archaeological finds include spades, ladders and other equipment, all well preserved in the salt, and dating back to the Iron Age. Other ancient deposits of common rock salt in Europe are in the region of Wieliczka near Krakow in Poland, where salt occurs in vast quantities with gypsum in salt clay.

   It is quite obvious that man has realised the importance of salt deposits right through the ages. However, its exact chemical composition was formulated by the British chemist and physicist Humphry Davy only in 1810.

   The main deposits of rock salt are in sea water. In all the oceans and seas of the world there must be approximately 20 million km^3 of salt, for sea water contains up to 3.7 per cent rock salt and other salts. This is why along sea coasts salt has been recovered down the ages by simple evaporation of salt water in flat tanks. This method of extrac-tion is particularly common in countries round the Mediterranean and Black Seas.

63   Halite — Wieliczka (Poland); actual size of crystals up to 9 cm

Deposits of rock salt in solid form are also found inland, in most geological formations. These were formed millions of years ago through the evaporation of salt water in drying sea basins under hot and arid climatic conditions. Salt gradually crystallised from water, thus forming the originally horizontal salt deposits, which subsequently often furrowed. The strongly plastic layers of rock salt thus formed enormous salt beds, which today are the chief sites of salt mining. The stratified deposits are sometimes several hundred metres thick and the salt is often associated with gypsum and anhydrite, and sometimes also with potassium salt.

Common rock salt forms granular to compact masses, and in fissures it often occurs as cubic crystals. They have a good cleavage. The salt stalagmites and stalactites which occur in some coal mines are of great interest from the mineralogical viewpoint. When chemically pure, salt is transparent; when it is grey the colouring is caused by clay, red colouring is caused by haematite, brown by bituminous matter, and blue by the presence of metallic sodium. Common rock salt often contains impurities such as magnesium or calcium chlorides. It is perfectly soluble in water.

The main producers of salt are the USA, Great Britain and Germany. The most notable deposits are the two already mentioned in Austria and Poland. Some very beautiful and interesting crystals form on the shores or surfaces of evaporating salt lakes such as the Dead Sea, Great Salt Lake in Utah and the salt lakes of North Africa. Crystal formations also occur in the steppe regions. The most beautiful crystals of rock salt are today found in the Siberian salt mines near Zashchita (Kazakhstan) and in some deposits in the USA, for example Lake Searles near San Bernardino in California. Crystals found in clusters in these deposits commonly reach a size of 2–6 cm, and individual crystals may have a size of up to 30 cm.

Salt is vital for human life. Each of us consumes an average of about 7.5 kg salt annually. A vast amount of salt is used today in the chemical industry, for which salt is an essential raw material, especially for the production of sodium compounds, chlorine and chlorine compounds. The large clear crystals are used in optics. The chief method of producing salt is by extraction from rock salt deposits, whereas the ancient, simple method of extraction from salt water is very much on the decline. The annual production of salt is approximately 35 million tonnes.

Sylvine (potassium chloride, KCl) crystallises similarly to rock salt, often with admixtures of sodium and magnesium chloride. It forms cubic, perfectly cleavable crystals or granular, occasionally also needle-shaped aggregates, which also have perfect cleavage. It may be colourless or whitish, bluish, or reddish to red in colour, and occurs in salt deposits, particularly at Stassfurt (Germany) and Kalusz (Poland). Sylvine is of great industrial importance, chiefly in the preparation of potash fertilisers (kainite, for example) and in the manufacture of potash soaps. Metallic potassium is used as a catalyst in the manufacture of synthetic rubber.

64   Halite — Hallstatt, Salzkammergut (Austria); actual size 10 x 8 cm

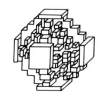

Fluorite (fluorspar) - *calcium fluoride*, CaF$_2$

Cubic; H. 3.5–4; Sp. gr. 3.1–3.2 g/cm^3; variously coloured, most commonly violet, green, yellow, less frequently colourless; vitreous lustre; S. colourless

Fluorite is a mineral which has always attracted attention because of the beauty of its crystals and variety of its colours. It caught the eye of the Erzgebirge miners in Bohemia who found it while mining for tin, and who called it 'the ore flower'. British miners in the Middle Ages also gave fluorite a poetic name: 'blue john'. Neither the Czech nor the British miners, however, were the first admirers of the magnificent colours and shapes of this mineral, for it had been used as an ornamental stone already by the ancient Greeks. They turned it in their workshops into beautiful multicoloured vessels, which later became famous as 'murrhine vases' (from the Latin *murrha* ='fluorite'). Natural fluorite was imported from Parthia (north-eastern region of modern Iran). During the time of the Roman Empire these vases were very highly valued. As there was a shortage of this rare mineral, glass imitations were produced by a special process; these are some of the first known imitations of precious gems.

Beautiful crystal specimens of fluorite occur fairly abundantly, very often with conspicuous colouring. The crystals have a perfect cleavage. They can form compact, granular or wiry aggregates. Colour may vary even within a single crystal or aggregate. When heated, fluorite emits a strong radiation (phosphorescence). In 1824, the German mineralogist Friedrich Mohs (1773-1839) discovered that fluorite exhibits a striking phenomenon which was later named fluorescence, after fluorite. This characteristic is particularly noticeable in some of the transparent fluorite varieties. The light that falls onto the mineral gives it a colour which is different from the colour the mineral has when

66   Fluorite — Durham (England); actual size of crystals 2–3 cm

the light passes through it: for example, in the incident light fluorites may be violet whereas in the passing light they are green (the term 'fluorescence' is now also applied to many different types of luminiscence).

Apart from occurring in deposits of tin ore, fluorite is often found in pegmatites and ore veins where it developed under high temperatures through crystallisation from hot solutions in association with volatile compounds escaping from magma. Fluorite of a sedimentary origin occurs less commonly and is found, for example, in cavities of limestone or in coal. The richest deposits of commercially important fluorite are of this category. They occur in the limestone beds of Kentucky and Illinois in the USA. In Europe, important deposits are at Freiberg in Saxony, at Weardale near Durham and in Derbyshire in the UK, in Switzerland (magnificent octahedrons in Alpine crevices), in France, Italy and Russia (also in the Transbaikal region in Siberia).

Fluorite is the most abundant natural compound and is used as a source of gaseous fluorine which was named after the mineral. There is still much to be learnt about fluorine as an element. Many of properties of its compounds are quite exceptional and it is sure to play an important role in the technical world of the future. Fluorine is an important industrial material. It is an aid in the smelting of some ores. Colourless fluorite is ground to make lenses which transmit ultraviolet rays. Fluorine and some of its compounds are poisonous, so they are used for disinfection purposes. Some compounds of fluorine are able to reduce temperatures to –100°C, for which they are used as refrigerants. Other compounds of fluorine are used for the manufacture of plastic materials. Fluorine is also an aid in separating uranium from its isotopes and in the aerospace technology. Fluorite can also be cut and polished as a less common gemstone.

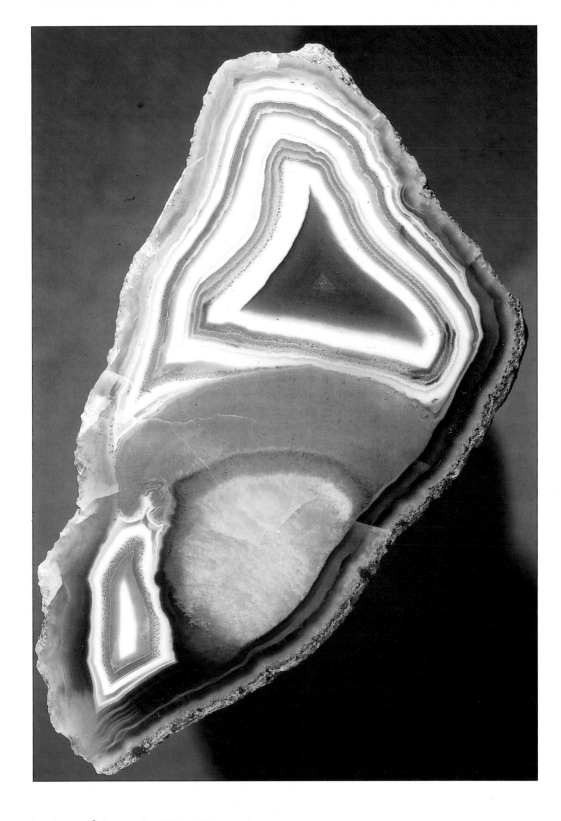

67　Agate — Železnice (Czech Republic); actual size 4 cm

Chapter 4

OXIDES

Oxides are compounds of oxygen with metallic or non-metallic elements. They are divided into anhydrous (such as quartz, cassiterite) and hydrous (opal, goethite) oxides. The spinel group — for example, spinel and magnetite (binary oxides with bivalent or trivalent elements) — are also classified as oxides, though in some old systems they were classified as an independent group. The different minerals of the spinel group mix together isomorphously. Another smaller group of minerals, which now comes under the heading of oxides, was once classed as the manganate group. These are also binary oxides, but unlike spinel they consist of tetravalent manganese and some bivalent elements (usually also manganese). Psilomelane is one such mineral. Under the new system wolframite is also classified as an oxide, though it used to be classified as a wolframate. The origin and occurrence of oxides are extremely varied.

Cuprite - *copper oxide*, Cu_2O

Cubic; H. 3.5–4;
Sp. gr. 5.8–6.2 g/cm³;
black-red;
adamantine
to submetallic lustre;
S. light red

68   Cuprite —
Liskeard, Cornwall
(UK); actual size of
crystal 8 mm

Cuprite was first described by Georgius Agricola in 1546 as a black mineral occurring in the surface layers of some copper ores. It is most frequently found in association with native copper. Its beautiful octahedral crystals of deep cochineal colour can be encountered in cavities of ore veins. In many deposits such octahedrons are accompanied by chalcotrichite (whose needles in reality are elongated tiny cubes of cuprite) or by other secondary copper minerals. This mineral was more accurately described by the French mineralogist, Romé de l'Isle in 1783; he referred to the renowned ore deposits in Cornwall in Great Britain and Timis in Romania. W. Haidinger, a Viennese mineralogist, gave the mineral the name cuprite in 1845 (from Latin *cuprum* ='copper').

Cuprite, which is commonly called red copper ore, can be compact, finely granular, massive or earthy; when needle-like, it is called chalcotrichite (from the Greek *chalkos*, 'copper', and *thrix*, 'hair'). Its natural ('fresh') colour is dark red with a diamond lustre but it assumes a steel grey shade. Cuprite mixed with limonite is red to brown-red in colour ('brick-red ore').

Cuprite originates as a product of incomplete oxidation of copper (cuprite pseudomorphs from native copper) or its sulphurous ores. As a result of weathering, cuprite changes into secondary copper carbonates (malachite and azurite), which in turn produce pseudomorphs. Main deposits: Moldova (on the Romanian side), Siegen in Rhineland (Germany), Sinjako in Bosnia, Chessy near Lyon (France), where octahedral crystals up to 3 cm in size occur, Nizhny Tagil in the Urals (Russia), Bisbee in Arizona, southern Australia, Bolivia, Onganja in Namibia. Next to native copper, cuprite is the richest copper ore with up to 88.8 per cent copper content. The transparent cuprite crystals are very valuable, but occur rarely.

Another anhydrous oxide of copper is known as tenorite, named in honour of M. Tenore (1780–1861), a botanist from Naples, or melaconite (from the Greek *melas*, 'black', and *konis*, 'dust'), or copper black. This is a copper oxide, CuO, and develops chiefly in black earthy aggregates on the surface of copper ores. Its monoclinic pseudohexagonal tabular crystals are a rare find. These are, in contrast to the powdery varieties, steel black in colour, with metallic lustre. The best known European deposits are in Italy on Vesuvius, near Siegen and Daaden in Germany, at Jáchymov in the Czech Republic, in several localities in Romania and, particularly, in Burgos province in Spain, where the mineral is fairly widespread. The largest deposits of tenorite are in the USA, especially in the vicinity of Bisbee, Arizona, where they form imposing asphalt-like layers, and by Lake Superior.

Spinel - *magnesium aluminium oxide*, $MgAl_2O_4$

Cubic; H. 8; Sp. gr. 3.5 g/cm³; variously coloured, most commonly red (ruby spinel), yellowish, bluish, pink (rubicelle); vitreous lustre; S. white

69   Cut spinels — Sri Lanka; actual size of largest stone 13.8 x 11.7 mm, weight 9.77 carat

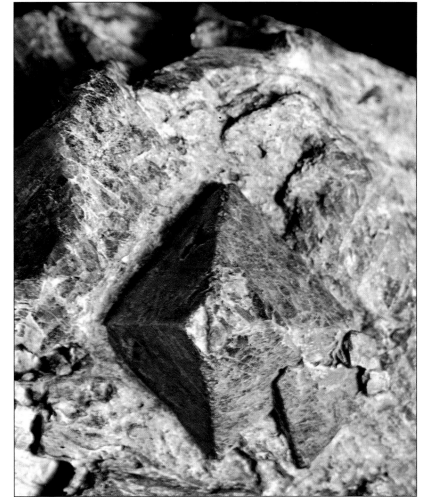

70 Spinel
(pleonaste) —
New York (USA);
actual size of
crystal 11 mm

Spinel apparently received its name from the Greek *spinther* ('spark'), and this was probably on account of the sparkling colours of its gemstone varieties. Spinel has been sought after and used for ornamental purposes since days of old, though it is less valuable than the ruby it resembles. Its crystals are usually smaller; bigger pieces are rare. A few are in the possession of the Natural History Museum in London. A 400-carat spinel is among the Moscow collection of state treasures, and a large scarlet spinel is among the English crown jewels. The most beautiful spinels are those in the Bohemian crown of St. Wenceslas.

Though various chemical impurities, particularly bivalent and trivalent iron and also chromium, do not disrupt the homogeneity of spinel's crystals, they affect its colouring. For example, red colour is caused by the presence of chromium, reddish-brown colour by trivalent iron, and bluish hues by bivalent iron. Mixtures of elements bring varied mixtures of colours. Chemically pure spinel, produced artificially, is colourless. Both bivalent and trivalent iron is present in substantial quantities in the black pleonaste, which frequently contains also chromium. Pleonaste is sometimes considered to be a different mineral. Many gem varieties of spinel are known by their common names used by jewellers, such as the blood-red ruby spinel, or the pink-red balas ruby, or the blue-red 'almandine spinel' and the hyacinth red to straw yellow rubicelle.

71 Magnetite —
Swiss Alps;
actual size
of crystal 2 cm

Magnetite - *ferrous-ferric oxide*, FeFe₂O

Cubic; H. 5.5; Sp. gr. 5.2 g/cm3; black with a bluish hue; metallic lustre; S. black

Magnetite is a mineral which justly deserves all the attention bestowed upon it by the ancient natural historians and philosophers, who were impressed by its magnetism. Pliny the Elder mentions magnetite: he writes about a hill near the river Indus, made entirely of stone and attracting iron. According to a fable, the stones were first discovered on this hill by a shepherd named Magnés, who noted that the nails of his boots and the iron ferrule of his staff adhered suddenly to the ground. It is said that magnetism, as a physical phenomenon, was named after this legendary figure. Another (more probable) version ascribes the name magnetite to the locality of its discovery: Magnesia, a region of ancient Thessaly (Greece).

Magnetite forms granular to compact masses, and occasionally it occurs in the form of octahedral crystals. It is strongly magnetic. Most common deposits are in the 'skarn' ores of igneous and metamorphic rocks. Magnetite, particularly in the skarns, is associated with silicates rich in iron — such as garnet andradite, pyroxene hedenbergite, various amphiboles, epidote and others. The most important and also most abundant sources of magnetite are the vast mountain formations in northern Sweden, Norway and the United States. The most beautiful crystals of magnetite have been found in Binnatal in Switzerland. Magnetite is the most valuable ore of iron and contains up to 72 per cent metal.

Chromite, an oxide of chromium and iron with some content of magnesium, is again a mineral in this group of binary cubic oxides. At first glance it is indistinguishable from magnetite but it is not magnetic and has a brown streak. Chromite is practically the sole chromium ore. Zimbabwe, South Africa, the Philippines and USA share in the world's production of chromite. Similar to chromite is franklinite, an oxide of iron and zinc with an admixture of manganese. It forms black octahedra, slightly rounded at the edges, which are embedded in white calcite. They occur at Franklin and Ogdenburg in New Jersey, USA.

Chrysoberyl - *beryllium aluminium oxide*, Al_2BeO_4

Orthorhombic; H. 8.6; Sp. gr. 3.7 g/cm³; yellow-green to yellow, alexandrite green in daylight, violet-red in artificial light; vitreous lustre; S. colourless

Chrysoberyl is not a widely known precious stone, and it is classed as one of the most valuable minerals. It occurs in pegmatites and in metamorphic rocks (for example those which developed through contact metamorphism). It usually crystallises in finely tabular and columnar form. Chrysoberyl is the third hardest mineral, next to diamond and corundum.

Of all the colourful and transparent varieties of this mineral, alexandrite is the most valuable one. It was named in honour of the Russian Tsar Alexander II. This stone is

72   Chrysoberyl — Maršíkov (Czech Republic); actual size of crystals up to 15 mm

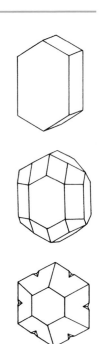

73   Cut chrysoberyl — Sri Lanka; actual size 18.8 x 17.4 mm; weight 27.81 carat

extremely unusual for being vividly green in daylight but mauve under artificial light. Because of this it is said that alexandrite is an emerald by day and an amethyst by night. This interesting phenomenon is caused by the absorption of certain colours of the light spectrum.

The chief chrysoberyl deposits are in Sri Lanka and Brazil (Espirito Santo state). Recently it has also been discovered at several places in Africa. Beautiful light green, perfectly transparent crystals are found for example by Lake Alaotra in Madagascar and extremely dark alexandrite crystals up to 2 cm in size in Zimbabwe. The best known European deposit is at Maršíkov near Sobotín (Czech Republic). Crystals from Maršíkov have a magnificent yellow colour but are too flat to be cut and polished. The alexandrite deposits in the valley of the Tokovaya river in the Urals, found in 1833, are world famous. Recently alexandrites have been found in other deposits of chrysoberyl in Sri Lanka and Brazil.

Larger crystals of chrysoberyl are found very rarely. The largest one, over 18 cm in size, was discovered near Golden in Jefferson county in Colorado, USA. Perfectly transparent crystals up to 10 cm in size have been found near Miakanjovata in Madagascar. Chrysoberyl specimens with a silky lustre (cymophanes) are sometimes found in fairly large lumps. After being cut to a lenticular shape, they exhibit a prominent, fluctuating lustre. They occur mainly in Sri Lanka and Brazil. The loveliest and largest group of alexandrite crystals was found in the Urals. It consists of a druse of 22 crystals, weighs 5 kg and measures 22 x 15 cm. This exquisite specimen can be viewed in the Mineralogical Museum of the Academy of Sciences in Moscow. A large individual alexandrite crystal was discovered in Sri Lanka. Cut and polished, it weighs 66 carats and is held in the collection of the Smithsonian Institution in Washington.

The price of alexandrites, particularly the perfectly transparent stones, is very high. A first-class 10-carat alexandrite would fetch as much as US$ 30,000 .

Corundum - *aluminium oxide*, Al_2O_3

Rhombohedral, H. 9; Sp. gr. 3.9–4.1 g/cm³; transparent (leucosapphire) or variously coloured; traces of chromic oxide cause red colouring (ruby), oxides of iron and titanium cause blue colouring (sapphire), also grey, green, yellow, brownish-red etc.; diamond lustre, and greasy lustre on less transparent crystals; S. white

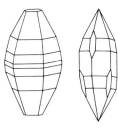

Corundum and its valuable transparent coloured varieties, including the ruby and sapphire, have a very long history of recognition as precious stones. The deposits of sapphire in Ratnapura, south-west of Colombo, Sri Lanka, have, for example, a history of several thousand years. In days of antiquity the robes of important Indian priests were adorned with sapphires. The first written references to the deposits of ruby come from the 6th century AD. They refer to the mines of Mogok in north Burma. It is, however, more than probable that precious stones were mined there much earlier, as in Sri Lanka.

During the Middle Ages, sapphires and especially rubies were widely used for the manufacture of jewellery. At that time these stones were ground into irregular shape of a carbochon — a cut with a round unfaceted top, particularly suitable for semitransparent or opaque stones. This method was applied because of the limitations of the cutting techniques of that time, and also in order to preserve as much of the precious material as possible. Sapphires and also a ruby cut in this manner can be seen, for example, in the Czech crown of St. Wenceslas, from 1346. This particular stone is the largest mounted ruby on record. Irregular in shape, it measures 39.5 x 36.5 x 14 mm and weighs approximately 250 carats. The greatest collections of large rubies and sapphires belong to the jewellery of Indian princes and of the Shah of Iran.

74   Ruby — Tanzania; actual size of detail 9 x 6 cm

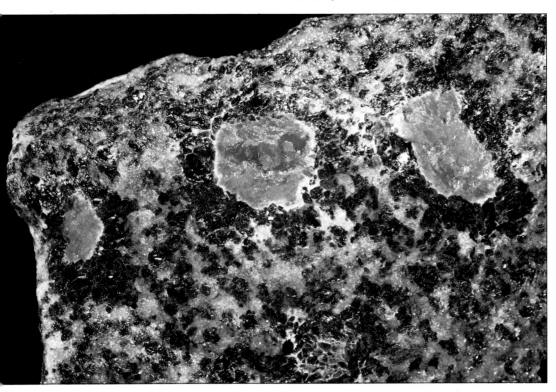

Corundum forms columnar barrel-shaped crystals and occasionally crystals which are tabular or needle-shaped. It is, however, most frequently granular or compact. Corundum deposits mostly occur in metamorphic rocks and in alluvia. For example, coarse-grained marbles in contact with granites and pegmatites form the parent rock of the Burmese rubies. In Sri Lanka, rubies and also sapphires are mainly found in alluvial deposits. Other deposits of rubies are in Thailand, India, Borneo, Australia, North Carolina (USA) and Madagascar. New deposits have been discovered in Kenya, Tanzania and Cambodia, where the deposits near Pailin look very promising.

Attractive, though not particularly transparent rubies have been found in the neighbourhood of Prilep in Macedonia (former Yugoslavia), where they occur in dolomitic marbles and often form rather unusually shaped crystals. The recently found Norwegian deposits sometimes yield ruby crystals of high gem quality. But these occur only rarely in nature. Asteriated rubies are interesting crystallographically, and are highly prized. When viewed from above by reflecting light, an asteriated mineral displays a six-pointed star, which is particularly noticeable when the stones have been cut into a lenticular shape.

The main deposits of sapphires are in Thailand, Kashmir, Australia and Montana (USA); others have recently been discovered in Tanzania and Cambodia. Smaller deposits exist in China and Madagascar. The best-known European deposit is at Jizerská louka (Czech Republic). Asteriated sapphires are again considered particularly interesting. Asterism is exhibited by sapphire crystals more commonly and to greater perfection than ruby crystals. However, in addition to rubies and sapphires, there are also other coloured gem varieties of corundum. White leucosapphire, for example, is used as an imitation diamond; and yellow corundum (or yellow sapphire) and the very rare mauve corundum are also very highly prized gemstones.

75   Corundum — cut yellow sapphire (Sri Lanka) and leucosapphire (Sri Lanka); actual size of yellow stone 14.4 x 8.7 mm, weight 10.69 carat

76   Corundum (cut ruby) — Mogok (Burma); actual size 14.5 mm in diameter, weight 27.12 carat

Besides being a much sought-for gemstone, corundum is an important mineral for industry, mainly because, next to diamond, it is the hardest mineral known. It also has a high mechanical and chemical resistance, very low expansivity, a high elasticity and a high melting point. It is not surprising that corundum has to be manufactured artificially to meet the increasing demand of both industrial users and jewellers. Synthetic rubies can be used, for example, in lasers.

Haematite (hematite) - *iron oxide*, Fe_2O_3

Rhombohedral; H.6.5; Sp. gr. 5.2–5.3 g/cm³; commonly red, crystallised dark grey, often with shady colours; metallic to submetallic lustre; S. red

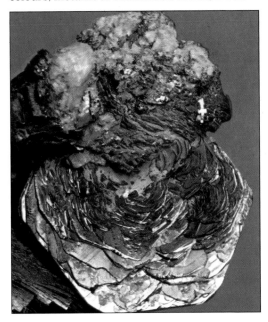

Haematite was known and mined in the ancient world. There is a reference to it in Virgil's *Aeneid*, where the poet (1st century BC) admires the beauty of the rhombohedral, brilliantly coloured crystals on the island of Elba. The colouring occurs through the refraction and dispersion of light in the surface layer of the mineral. Lump haematite was also used for ornamental purposes, and was particularly popular with the Babylonians and Egyptians, as shown by archaeological finds.

Haematite occurs in the most varied forms and in an extensive range of colours, but the colour of its streak is always red. The term 'haematite' usually refers to the crystallised and crystalline varieties, harder than those known in some languages as 'blood stones', which are lump, granular, filamentous and

77 Haematite — St. Gotthard (Switzerland); actual size 7 cm

78 Haematite — Bludná, near Horní Blatná (Czech Republic); actual size 7 x 6 cm

earthy. Iron mica is foliated haematite, which occurs in agglomerates, commonly in association with quartz. The scaly, stratified and rock-forming variety is called iron mica schist or itabirite (thus named after the deposits in the Itabira range, Brazil). The most common variety is fine-grained ochre. Oolitic haematite, which originated through deposition on the seafloor, is of particularly high practical value.

Haematite develops under the most varied natural conditions. It is, after all, one of the most abundant minerals — the red colour of soil, gravel and whole rocks is caused by its presence. The name 'haematite' is derived from the red colour (*haima* in Greek means 'blood'). Apart from sedimentary rocks, it also occurs in metamorphic deposits, and in small quantities it is found in hydrothermal veins, magmatic rocks and in oxidation zones.

The richest world deposits of haematite are in Sweden, Russia (Kursk) and the Ukraine (Krivoi Rog). The so-called 'Alpine roses' form beautiful clusters of flat crystals in Alpine deposits, for example, at St. Gotthard. The British and Bohemian kidney ores (a variety of haematite which forms reniform aggregates) are used for making precious stones for rings and necklaces. As an iron ore, haematite contains about 70 per cent metal. The red ochre variety is used in making pigments and in polishing and grinding.

Quartz - *silicon dioxide*, SiO_2

Rhombohedral-pseudohexagonal; H. 7; Sp. gr. 2.65 g/cm^3; for colour see text; S. colourless, white to grey

Quartz was well known to the ancient world, especially the purest variety — rock crystal. The word 'crystal' is of Greek origin and means 'ice'. Quartz also resembles ice and stays cold for a long time in warm conditions, unlike glass, for instance. This is because quartz is a very poor conductor of heat. Ancient Romans knew this, too, and wealthy patricians often had large crystal balls in their homes, which were there to cool their hands. Pliny the Elder was struck by this particular characteristic of rock crystal and opined that rock crystal originated from ice in such freezing conditions that it could not melt even in the most intensive heat. The Greeks and Romans were well aware of other quartz

79 Quartz — Cínovec, near Teplice (Czech Republic); actual size 16 x 10 cm

80   Amethyst — Cavnic (Romania); actual size of crystals 3.5 cm

varieties, though they had no idea that they were all the same mineral. Quartz served
humans much earlier than this, firstly because it was so widely abundant and resistant
to weathering and all external effects. It was without doubt the first mineral to be used
by humans as a weapon and an essential tool in their fight for existence. Implements
made of flint (a variety of quartz) were used from the beginning of the Palaeolithic

81 Smoky quartz —
St. Gotthard
(Switzerland);
actual size of the
large crystal 11 cm

period to the end of the Neolithic period, which happened at the beginning of the 2nd millennium BC.

Quartz has been useful to humans through history, and is still so today. Prehistoric humans valued flint for its toughness, resistance to wear and for its sharp cutting edges. Gradually down the ages a number of other excellent qualities of quartz were discovered, so its usefulness grew and today it is widely used in modern industrial manufacture.

Even in ancient times miners were amazed by the beauty of quartz crystals. As cultures advanced, the popularity of quartz and its varieties increased: its beautiful shapes and splendid colours caused it to be very much in demand as a precious and ornamental stone. The magnificently cut goblets from the Middle Ages which were made by famous masters of that era (especially Italians and Germans) command our admiration even today. (The most beautiful goblets were once concentrated in the collections of Emperor Rudolf II in Prague). Present-day works of art seldom match the beauty and perfectness of these medieval artefacts.

The material was supplied mainly from the Alpine deposits. The largest clear crystals were taken to Prague, where the craftsmen who worked for Emperor Rudolf II — a generous supporter of art and *maximus adorator et amator gemmarum* — enhanced their beauty by turning them into magnificent works of art. Many of them are at present kept in the collections of world museums, in Vienna, for example.

It is apparent from the jewellery and ornamental objects of the Middle Ages and the Renaissance that the various quartz varieties were extremely popular stones. Their very impressive perfect transparency and strong lustre made them much in demand, and they often replaced other precious stones which were rarer and less accessible.

Quartz appears in the mineral kingdom in the most varied forms, either as crystals or in massive aggregates. Apart from the clear, glassy rock crystal there are many varieties of distinctive colour. Amethyst is a very popular crystal variety, with a beautiful purple to red-violet colour. It owes its colouring to radioactive irradiation and to an iron admixture. The colouring of the amethysts from some deposits is not constant in daylight, and fades fairly quickly. Amethyst was familiar to the ancient Greeks and Romans who believed that it was a remedy for drunkenness (its name is derived from the Greek *amethystos*, 'unintoxicating'). They used it in the production of expensive amulets and decorative objects.

Citrine is a crystallised quartz, with a pale yellow colour caused by the presence of iron trioxide. Smoky quartz is another crystallised quartz variety, distinguishable by its smoky brown to brown-black colour. The black, almost opaque variety of smoky quartz is morion — this comes from the Latin *mormorion* originally used by Pliny the Elder for

82   Rose quartz — Brazil; actual size 12 x 9 cm

the black jaspers and onyxes imported from India. The colouring of both these varieties is, for the most part, caused by the silicon ions being released from their positions in the crystal structure during radioactive decay. It is usually removed by careful firing.

The most popular massive quartz variety is rose quartz, in various shades of pink — from pale pink to rose pink, sometimes with a violet hue. This colour is due to the presence of manganese oxide and fades when the mineral is heated to 575°C. Prolonged exposure to the atmosphere also causes the colour to fade. Until recently, rose quartz was known only in massive form, but a few years ago deposits were found in Brazil where it occurs in crystal form.

Prase, named from the Latin *prasius* ('leek green'), is a green lump quartz which owes its colour to the presence of many actinolite needles. The pleasant shade made it a desirable stone in ancient times in the manufacture of gems and mosaics. Sapphire quartz is another lump quartz variety, blue-green in colour, whose colour is due to the presence of numerous needles of fibrous blue amphibole-crocidolite.

83 Ferruginous quartz — Hořovice (Czech Republic); actual size 7 x 6.5 cm

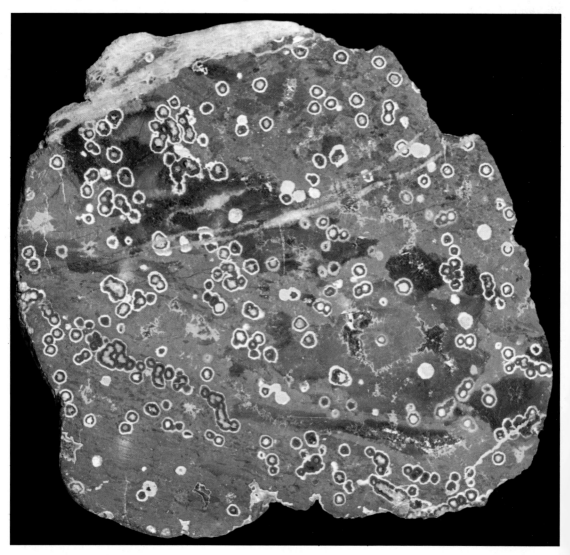

84   Tiger's eye — Griquatown (South Africa); actual size 9 x 6 cm

Red, brown or yellow, ferruginous quartz is massive, granular or crystallised. Milky quartz has no impurities but is clouded to a milky white colour and is a veinstone. The milkiness is caused by the presence of a multitude of tiny air cavities which refract light. The impure varieties of a wide range of colours are classed as common quartz. Grey hornstone is a mixture of quartz and chalcedony, and so is the similar flint, which is darker, even black.

The fibrous, banded quartz varieties are well known in the jewellery trade and are very popular. Their pleasing colouring and lustre, which improve with cutting and polishing, are caused by amphibole fibres, especially crocidolite. According to their colouring, there are grey-green cat's eyes, blue-grey falcon's eyes, and tiger's eyes with yellow fibres of weathered crocidolite.

Aventurine is an exception. It is massive and contains a multitude of minute scales of mica or haematite which are responsible for the characteristic sparkle of the mineral. It is of interest that imitations of this stone existed before the stone itself was discovered. It so happened that in the workshop of a Venetian glassmaker at Murano, glass material of an exceptional lustre, caused by the inclusion of minute copper flakes, was created almost by accident (*per avventura*, as they say in Italian). This material was named aventurine and was sold under this name; when later on a mineral of similar appearance was discovered, it was given the same name.

Apart from the crystallised, granular and massive quartz varieties already mentioned, there are many others, which are distinguishable by the varied growth of their crys-tals. Individual crystals and crystal aggregates, which originated mainly from hot solutions, and which differ in form in various ways, belong to this group. Cap quartz, for example, is crystallised quartz, in which small layers of intruding matter, such as mica, formed during its interrupted growth. Such a crystal can be split with one blow into a number of little 'caps'. Star quartz consists of individual crystals grouped in

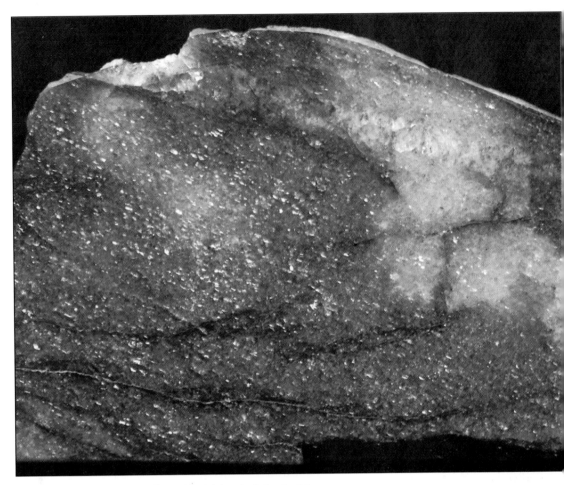

85   Aventurine quartz — Styria (Austria); actual size 8 x 5.5 cm

a star-shaped cluster. The so-called token quartz, which occurs mostly as a veinstone or in fissures of crystalline schists, has crystals which form in the following manner: the original columnar crystal narrows at the end and another, somewhat wider crystal grows into it where it terminates; it is usually bounded on both sides and is always oriented in the same direction as the slender crystal underneath.

Porphyritic quartz occurs as crystals formed from the smelt of some porphyritic rocks which are bounded only by rhombohedral faces but no prismatic faces (called dihexahedra). Babylonian quartz develops in shapes which are narrowed at the top, stone-wall quartz forms crystals which are intergrown on parallel lines and which display patterns

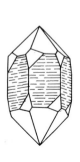 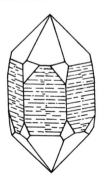   

resembling stone walls when they are broken transversally. Honeycomb quartz occurs as a covering pseudomorph after the dissolution of original minerals, which left behind only surface crusts of quartz.

Quartz crystals are normally very pretty. They are mostly hexagonal prisms, terminated by two rhombohedra. The angle between the prism faces always remains 60°, regardless of the crystal's development. The prism faces are usually horizontally striated. The striation is because of ridges alternating between the prisms and the rhombohedron during the growth of the crystal. The conditions during crystallisation are by no means always ideal. Such side effects as pressures or increased flow of solutions can cause crystals to grow distorted. Yet the angle at which individual faces intersect always remains constant. Nicolaus Stensen, a Danish physician and geologist,

86   Token amethyst — Banská Štiavnica (Slovakia); actual size of the large crystal 7 cm

studied the angles of quartz and published the results of his investigations in 1669, formulating them as the law of constancy of angle on crystals of one mineral. With this he became the founder of scientific crystallography.

There are some giant specimens among quartz crystals. These come particularly from Madagascar, where individual crystals have been found with a circumference of several metres.

One can frequently find in quartz quite a number of small cavities, partially or completely filled with the parent solution from which quartz crystallised. Study of such cavities reveals much about the conditions under which quartz developed in each individual deposit.

Quartz is the commonest and the most widely occurring mineral, responsible for 12 per cent of the composition of the Earth's crust. Apart from this, there is about 47 per cent silicon dioxide in various forms of silicates, which are the chief rock-forming minerals. Quartz is a substantial component of many igneous rocks (for example, the greyish grains of granite) and of metamorphic rocks (gneisses, mica schists and quartzites).

Fairly large quartz crystals are found mainly in cavities of coarse-grained granites, in pegmatites, in some ore veins and in crystalline schists. In ore veins they commonly develop in gangue, though entire quartz veins are also common. Crystals of clear quartz (rock crystal) usually occur in crevices of schists, but also in igneous rocks, such as melaphyres, often jointly with agates. Amethyst, too, can be found in cavities of igneous rocks, where it forms geodes — round-shaped stones with a hollow centre. It is also recovered from the gangues of ore veins and from quartz veins. Smoky quartz and morion occur similarly. Rose quartz usually forms in pegmatites.

Hornstone occurs in ore veins as a mineral of inorganic origin; flint occurs as nodules of organic origin in Mesozoic (Jurassic and Cretaceous) sedimentary rocks. As a mineral highly resistant to weathering and decomposition, it often finds its way into

87   Amethyst — Porcura (Romania); actual size of crystals up to 3 cm

88   Cut amethysts — Brazil; actual size of larger stone 51.5 mm in diameter, weight 361.5 carat

screes, gravel beds or alluvials. Quartz is therefore in great abundance in many sedimentary rocks.

It is obvious that quartz originates in many varied ways. It crystallises anywhere between the highest temperatures of volcanic magma and the normal temperature of the Earth's surface, from hot solutions or solutions comparatively cool.

The most magnificent quartz crystals, expecially clear quartz, come from Alpine schists. In 1719 an enormous cavity was discovered in Zinggenstock, near Grimsel Pass in the Bernese Alps of Switzerland. More than 100 tonnes of the most beautiful clear crystals have been extracted from this 'crystal cellar'. Some pieces weighed as much as 800 kg. The richest crystal deposits at the present time are in the eastern and northeastern part of Madagascar, southern Brazil (the surroundings of Cristallina in the mountain range of Serra dos Cristaes in the state of Goiás) and also Arkansas in the United States. In Arkansas in the Hot Springs area a cavity 2 x 10 m in size was discovered from which wagon loads of clear quartz were recovered. In Madagascar rocks up to 50 kg in weight are extracted; the largest known pieces of rock crystal come from these deposits. The Brazilian crystals are sometimes more than 0.5 m in thickness. In the Carpathian mountains of western Ukraine there are deposits of little crystals called 'Marmarosh diamonds' from Tertiary sandstones and schists (called flysch). They occur as individual loose crystals and are bounded on both sides. The crystals of rock crystal found in cavities of the famous snow-white Carrara marble in northern Italy are considered the most perfectly bounded specimens. Similar to them are the loose crystals, called Harkimer diamonds, from Harkimer near New York.

The largest amethyst geode was found in 1900 in Rio Grande do Sul in Brazil. It measured 10 x 5 x 3 m and weighed 7 tonnes. Parts of this geode can be seen in a number of museums. Similar, though much smaller pockets of crystallised quartz varieties are found near Idar-Oberstein in Germany and in the foothill area on the Czech side of the Riesengebirge (Giant Mountains). The most valuable amethyst deposits, apart from Rio Grande do Sul, are in adjoining Uruguay, in Mexico and in Madagascar (Be-

89   Citrine — Rio
Grande do Sul (Brazil);
actual size 14 x 9 cm

tafo), where particularly richly coloured stones are extracted. The loveliest European amethysts come from the Urals (Murzinka) and from the ore veins of the Carpathian mountains, especially near Cavnic in Romania and near Banská Štiavnica in Slovakia (also token quartz). However, the colour of the amethysts from Banská Štiavnica fades fairly quickly when they are exposed to daylight.

There are valuable deposits of smoky quartz and morion in the Alps, particularly in the vicinity of St. Gotthard, where they form in pockets in granite rocks. In 1868, a cavity 6 x 4 x 2 m in size, containing 30 tonnes of smoky quartz, was discovered in the Swiss canton of Uri. The largest of these specimens are on show in the Natural Science Museum in Bern (the biggest crystal is 70 cm long and weighs 130 kg). Magnificent druses of smoky quartz occur in the Urals (Murzinka), in southern Brazil, in Madagascar and in Colorado, USA. Attractive smoky quartz crystals also occur in the Czech Republic, especially in pegmatites at Dolní Bory near Velké Meziříčí in Moravia.

Natural citrine is comparatively rare (it occurs, for example, in western Moravia). The most beautiful pieces come from Brazil and the Urals. Most of the citrines available on the market are artificially heated amethyst or smoky quartz. They are sold under the names of 'gold topaz', 'Spanish topaz, 'Madeira topaz', or 'topaz from the Urals'.

The localities of rose quartz deposits are Madagascar (massive) and Brazil (crystallised). In Europe they occur comparatively amply in pegmatites in Bavaria (Germany) and in the Urals (Russia).

Massive ferruginous quartz occurs in some iron ore deposits near Hořovice (Czech Republic), and is found in crystal form at Iserlohn in Westphalia, Germany. Green aventurine quartz was in great demand in China and was named 'the imperial stone Yu'. Aventurine is also found abundantly in the Urals (vicinity of Miass), in Siberia, Tibet, India, and — in Europe — in Styria (Austria). Quartz penetrated with fibrous minerals is not frequently found in deposits. Cat's eye occurs chiefly in Sri Lanka and the popular and once also valuable tiger's eye and falcon's eye in the Doorn range (Asbestos Mountain) in South Africa. Similar deposits also exist in China, Australia and in the Ukraine (Krivoi Rog).

Clear quartz (rock crystal), which is as hard and tough as other quartz varieties, is today used chiefly in making larger art objects. Amethyst is most sought after and is widely used for making jewellery and decorative objects. Its most valuable crystals have rich and consistent colours. When heated to approximately 250°C some amethysts get a rich honey yellow colour. It did not take long for jewellery manufacturers to take advantage of this and to turn the stones into artificial citrines, which are choice precious stones often mistaken for topaz. Exposure to radioactive radiation returns the stones to their original violet colour.

Amethysts, citrines, smoky quartz, clear quartz and sometimes even rose quartz are ground to a brilliant cut of elongated, oval or a round shape. Smoky quartz, morion and amethyst are particularly suitable as larger ring stones. A number of quartz varieties are also a suitable material for glyptics, that is, for carving and engraving either with a raised design (cameo) or incised design (intaglio).

Transparent quartz with interesting inclusions is very popular in the making of jewellery. Such inclusions may be flakes of green chlorite, needles of actinolite, tourmaline or brown rutile — sagenite (*fléches d'amour*). They are often sold at a comparatively high price to tourists in regions where they occur (such as the Alps). The same applies to crystallised quartz specimens, especially those of clear quartz (rock crystal), which are often accompanied by other interesting minerals such as adularia, chlorites or various titanium minerals. Alpine crystal hunters (called *Strahler* in German) scale the most dangerous places in order to trace the course of quartz veins. They determine the position of vein cavities with a tap of the hammer and proceed to open them with a pickaxe, using all their expertise. These cavities often occur in the most dangerous and

90   Cut citrines — Brazil; actual size of largest stone 54.6 x 49.1 mm, weight 374 carat

91   Star quartz —
Peřimov, near
Jilemnice (Czech
Republic); actual
size 15 x 13 cm

inaccessible positions. The crystal hunters are sometimes lucky enough to be the first to discover the breathtaking magnificence of the true crystal caves, whose walls are lined with pure, clear crystals, or with smoky quartz crystals of fairy-tale loveliness. The greatest number of Strahlers operate in Switzerland.

Today quartz is an important raw material for the glass and optical industries. The transparent, pure clear quartz is used in the manufacture of optical glass. A major and unusual use of quartz is in radio-engineering, but most of the quartz crystals serving these purposes are manufactured artificially today. They are used for various optical instruments (polarising microscopes, instruments to identify minerals, spectroscopic instruments, astronomical telescopes etc.). The importance of the synthetic production of quartz keeps increasing, because the natural deposits of rock crystal needed for technical purposes can no longer meet the growing demand and will be soon exhausted. Artificial clear crystal is valuable for all the needs of industry, especially for electronic equipment, which demands not only a perfectly pure material but first and foremost a material with a perfect internal structure of a crystal which is not twinned (monocrystal). This requirement is not usually met in natural crystals, even those which are perfectly suitable for use as gemstones, because most of them occur as twinned crystals. It is understandable, then, that the demand for synthetic quartz crystals is exceedingly high in all technically developed countries. In the United States, for example, the consumption of quartz crystals is about 3000 tonnes a year; these are worth about $18 million.

Mixture of rhombohedral quartz, cryptocrystalline chalcedony and colouring impurities; H. approx. 7; Sp. gr. variable; red, ochre yellow, green; dark, greasy to vitreous lustre; S. white to grey

Jasper is one of the precious and decorative stones used in the ancient world. In fact, in the past jasper's popularity was far greater than now. Jasper was used for making ornaments and amulets. The ancient Egyptians, Greeks and Romans used various methods for boring holes into the stones and for engraving different symbols, signs and later even portraits on their surfaces. This was the beginning of glyptic art. Jasper also decorated the Jewish high priest's plate (called *jashfe*). Pliny also wrote about the colourful splendour of jaspers.

Jasper's popularity lasted through the Middle Ages. In Bohemia, the chapels of Karlštejn castle and the St. Wenceslas chapel of St. Vitus cathedral in Prague have walls partially decorated with blood red jaspers. The decoration dates from the reign of Emperor Charles IV who, in 1347, had all his favourite places decorated with jaspers. At that time, jaspers and amethysts were being extracted from veins on the Czech side of the Erzgebirge (Ore Mountains), near Ciboušov, then transported to Prague for cutting and polishing. Specially selected discs were embedded in mortar and rimmed with gold.

The book *Gemmarum et lapidum historia*, by de Boot, the personal surgeon to Emperor Rudolf II, discusses the popularity of jasper during the Renaissance period. De Boot describes, for example, a large table top from the Emperor's collection made up of a multitude of coloured jaspers obtained from deposits in the Czech foothills of the Giant Mountains: it depicted a landscape and was then considered one of the seven wonders of the world. During that period there were many works of art created from Bohemian jaspers, though not so famous as the one just mentioned.

The Hermitage Museum in St. Petersburg (once the Winter Palace of the Tsars) holds a wealth of objects made from jasper in its halls and chambers. There are pillars and vases measuring several metres, often carved from a single piece of the mineral, made by craftsmen cutters in the well known Russian workshops of Petrodvorets and Ekaterinburg. Rich deposits near Orsk in the Urals yielded the minerals for this purpose. Jaspers found in that locality are still known for their striking gaiety of colours. Magnificently carved Indian jaspers can also be found in the collections of Indian maharajas.

Pliny used the term 'jasper' for the lighter types of the mineral. At the same time, he named a number of the coloured varieties; the dark to black jaspers from India

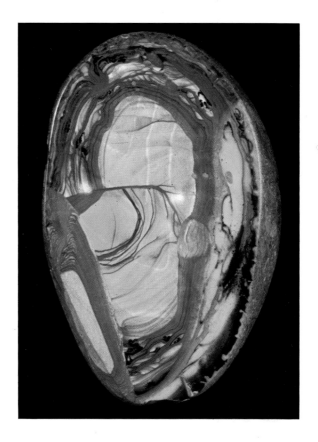

92   Jasper — Mokkatam (Egypt); actual size 9.5 x 5.5 cm

93 Jasper — Kozákov (Czech Republic); actual size 15 x 9 cm

were originally classed as 'morion'. This name was later applied to dark smoky quartz. Green jasper with regular, red-blood haematite stains was called heliotrope from the Greek *helios* ('sun') and *trepa* ('to change'), for in ancient times this stone was used for observing the movements of the sun.

Jaspers occur frequently under natural conditions; they are inseparable companions of agates and chalcedony. They develop mainly through crystallisation of hot solutions in cracks of igneous rocks, usually melaphyres. The mineral components of these igneous rocks were, after consolidation of the rock, decomposed again through the effect of hot solutions. The siliceous gel, which was freed by this, was carried into the cracks. There it crystallised into fine-grained to compact opaque quartz together with chalcedony; these, together with additional mineral colouring substances, are the basic components of jasper. Powdery haematite gives them a red colour, limonite dyes them brown to yellow and the mossy chlorite aggregates turn them green. Sometimes jaspers are formed through the metamorphism of sedimentary rocks, caused by the hot melaphyre lava.

Jaspers also form variously shaped concretions (tubers) in some sedimentary rocks, for example in Egyptian limestones, and are freed by their weathering. These interesting chestnut brown or coffee brown jasper cobbles, also called 'Nile quartz', have a strong lustre and a somewhat unusual surface produced by grains of sand being hurled against them by the desert winds. When cut and polished, they are indeed an attractive sight, for they are usually beautifully banded and decorated with black branching tree-like shapes (dendrite shapes), which resemble fossilised moss. They are used in making souvenirs and ornamental objects.

The foothills on the Czech side of the Erzgebirge yield abundant magnificent jaspers (at Kozákov, for example). Notable occurrences are in the southern Urals (Russia), from where jasper boulders weighing hundreds of kilograms have been recovered. German jasper is also well known, especially from the Rhineland (Idar-Oberstein) and many localities in Saxony (the valley of the river Müglitz and environs of the town of Chemnitz). Large deposits also occur in India, Brazil and in the Egyptian desert near the Nile. Heliotrope is found in many Indian deposits. It occurs together with other jasper varieties more or less in the same places as agates and chalcedony; together with them it is worked by the local gemcutters, or exported to Europe. Deposits of jasper have also been found recently in Madagascar.

Jasper as a raw material is suitable for the manufacture of a large variety of objects, especially ornamental ones, for a number of good reasons: it shows a high chemical and physical resistance, it is easily accessible, occurs in large, unblemished pieces and, last but not least, it has a very attractive appearance. This material has been used for making a variety of small objects since ancient times, such as elegantly curved handles, clips and slides and ornamental buttons, as well as more valuable objects, with exquisite carvings and engravings, such as brooches, rings, earrings, necklaces and pendants. In Europe the Czech foothills of the Giant Mountains were a world renowned centre for cutting and working these stones. The industry continued thriving until the arrival of jasper, agates and quartz from deposits in Brazil and Uruguay. They came to the workshops of Idar-Oberstein in the Rhineland; superior in size, and more abundant in supply, they soon pushed the Czech products out of the European market. Jaspers are now widely used in Russia and in some parts of North America, mostly for the manufacture of dishes, goblets, paperweights and mosaics. The finest pieces are also used for making gemstones.

94   Jasper — Kabamba (Madagascar); actual size 10 x 7cm

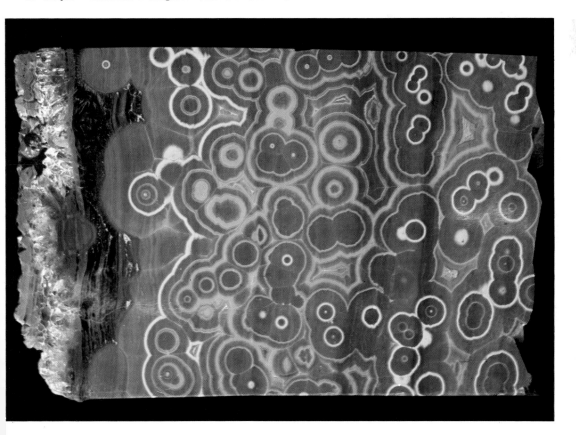

Chalcedony - *silicon dioxide*, SiO_2

Rhombohedral-cryptocrystalline; H. 6.5; Sp. gr. 2.59–2.61 g/cm³; variously coloured, most commonly grey, yellow-red (carnelian, sard) or green (plasma and chrysoprase), often speckled; greasy to vitreous lustre; S. white to grey

Chalcedony was a very familiar mineral to ancient civilisations. In those days it was a most popular and sought-after stone, especially in Egypt, Greece and Asia Minor. The ancient Egyptians excelled in the art of gem cutting, engraving and polishing. Specimens of chalcedony scarabs, inscribed with hieroglyphs, representing the beetle *Ateuchus sacer*, which were worn as amulets have been preserved to the present day. They have been found, together with other jewels and precious stones, in the tombs of mummies mainly in the vicinity of Thebes.

Chalcedony was so named after the ancient city of Chalcedon (now Kalkidoy) near Istanbul, where it was discovered. Many chalcedony varieties were recognised already in ancient times, for example the red carnelian (from the Latin *carneus,* 'meaty') or the green plasma. Today's name of plasma comes from the Italian language but originally it denoted any worked green stones from the ruins of ancient Rome.

During the Middle Ages, chrysoprase, a pleasantly apple-green chalcedony, whose name is derived from the Greek *chrysos* ('golden'), was quite a valuable ornamental stone. During the reign of the Hapsburg Emperor Rudolf II the demand for chalcedony was so great that the emperor himself sent collectors to the deposits beneath the Erzgebirge: these people were specially commissioned by the emperor and had many privileges over ordinary people.

95 Chalcedony — Tri Vody (Slovakia); actual size of detail 15 x 12 cm

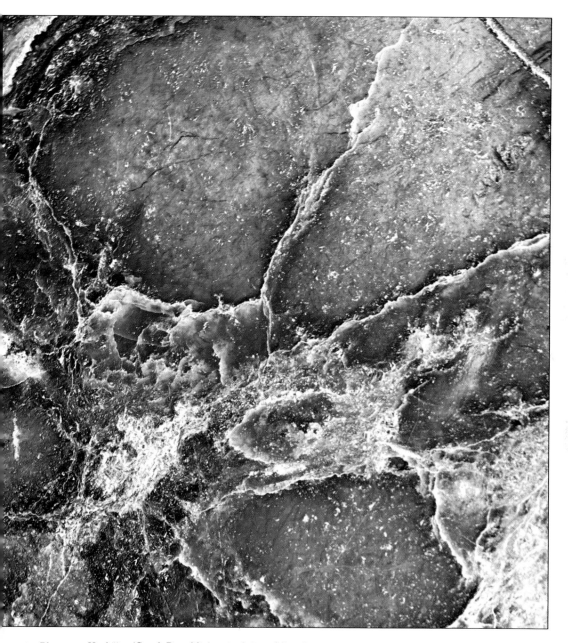

96   Plasma — Hrubšice (Czech Republic); actual size of detail 6 x 6 cm

Chalcedony is a very interesting variety of quartz, which differs from other varieties by its characteristics and the mode of its origin, for it comes from gelatinous siliceous matter. Externally, chalcedony appears to be a compact mineral, but an examination under the microscope shows that it is an aggregate of extremely fine, closely packed fibres, which form either layers or round aggregates (spherulites). As a micro-crystalline quartz, chalcedony has a number of varieties, which differ from each other in their optical properties.

Chalcedony usually forms layers with a reniform surface and an even to splintery fracture; these layers are always clouded and just translucent (they have the colour of an opaque medium). Chalcedony very often develops with opal and a variety of

97 Moss agate — Železnice, near Jičín (Czech Republic); actual size 9 cm

mineral pigments such as haematite, limonite, chlorite and others. The fine pores between the fibres — if they are large enough — enable chalcedony and its different varieties to be artificially coloured. The methods of artificial dyeing were once carefully guarded secrets but today most of them are commonly known and used in stone working practice. Chalcedony has a great number of varieties, distinguished by their colour and structure.

Collectors' names for the different coloured varieties of chalcedony are often quite unnecessary from the mineralogical viewpoint, but they are commonly known and widely used. Carnelian is tinted red with oxides of iron. Carnelian itself has a special variety, the orange-coloured sard, which is a highly valued gemstone. Plasma is coloured green by minerals containing chlorite.

Moss agate is a chalcedony containing small dendrites, which are either oxides of iron or manganese (brown or black), or chlorite (green). Cacholong is a chalk-white mixture of chalcedony and opal. Its name, of Mongolian origin, means 'a beautiful stone'. Chrysoprase is an apple-green chalcedony coloured with nickel oxide. The common chalcedony forms grey, bluish or yellowish translucent aggregates.

The richest and largest occurrences of chalcedony are in cracks and holes of melaphyre and amygdoidal lava, which solidified on the Earth's surface. The numerous holes in these rocks were formed

98   Moss agate — Collyer, Kansas (USA); actual size of detail 12 x 9 cm

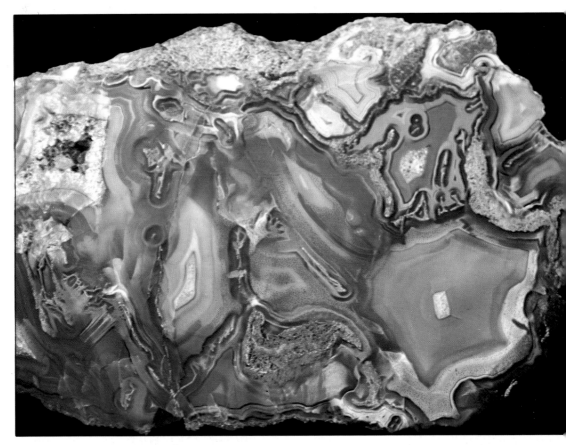

99　Agate — India; actual size 28 x 17 cm

gradually by the escaping gases and were filled by the secondary siliceous gel. Today such chalcedony concretions (the fillings of these holes) are found not only in the original rock, but also in gravels and in topsoil, which developed through the weathering of igneous rocks. They also occur in the alluvials of streams and rivers, which often carry them far away.

Primary and secondary deposits of this type occur in Brazil, Uruguay and in India (with particularly rich deposits in Dekkan). The main European deposits are in Germany (Idar-Oberstein in the Rhineland), in the foothill area on the Czech side of the Giant Mountains, in Iceland and the Faeroes.

Chalcedony can also originate in most deposits from the decomposition of silicates. This frequently happens in the surface layers of ore deposits, as in Styria (Erzberg), in Slovakia and in Sardinia (La Speranza). Beautifully shaped small chalcedony stalactites and stalagmites can be seen at these sites, with their transparently white to pale blue colouring, and often forming miniature caves. Plasma results similarly through the weathering of serpentines, frequently in association with opal. Chalcedony can be found in various other places, such as in clayey siderites, in coal deposits, or in siliceous concretions of sedimentary rocks (some of the cacholongs).

Carnelian occurs mainly in Brazil and India (the loveliest carnelians come from the hinterland of Bombay). In Europe it is found in the foothills of the Giant Mountains (Czech Republic), and in Transylvania (Romania). Carnelian was discovered in Arabia and Egypt in ancient times, and so was sardonyx in Asia Minor. The stones found in those deposits were highly valued as precious gems. The most noted occurrences of moss agate are in India (green), the Urals (green and black), and the town of Mocha (or Al Mukna) in Yemen (black). The latter were exported to Europe under the name of 'Mocha stones'.

Cacholong occurs abundantly in the Mongolian deserts, in the basalt rocks beneath the Giant Mountains and in the cavities of quartz concretions of the Mesozoic Era in the Moravian Karst. The best deposits of chrysoprase are at Kozmice in Polish Silesia and in Australia. Some chalcedony specimens from Uruguay are rather interesting, for they contain liquid remains (the mother liquor); such specimens are called enhydros (from the Greek *hydor*, 'water').

Chalcedony, like agate or jasper, is used in the manufacture of a great variety of ornamental objects. Chalcedony and its varieties are very popular with collectors. Because of its hardness and chemical resistance, which differs only slightly from that of quartz, massive pieces of chalcedony serve as an excellent raw material from which to make bearings and edges for sensitive scales, compasses and other instruments, pestles and mortars for chemists. Finely ground chalcedony is used for polishing various hard surfaces and for filling some soaps. Powdered chalcedony is also added to dyes and enamels.

Agate - *silicon dioxide*, SiO_2

Mixture of cryptocrystalline chalcedony, rhombohedral quartz and shapeless opal; H. approx. 7; Sp. gr. variable; colour — see text; S. white to grey

Agate is, and has always been, among the most popular precious stones. It was first mentioned in writing by the Greek philosopher, surgeon and natural scientist, Theophrastus (376–287 BC), but of course the stone was known and used long before that.

100   Agate — Brazil; actual size 10 x 6.5 cm

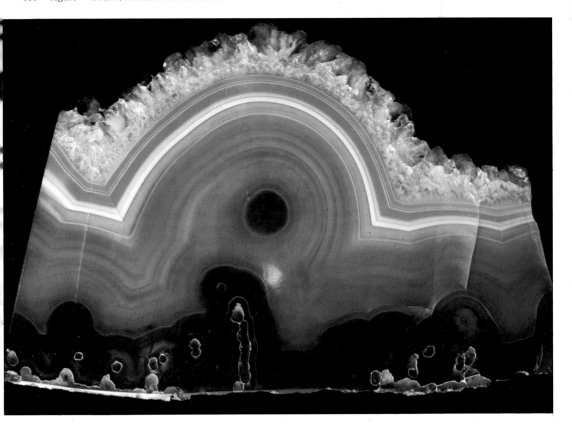

Theophrastus gave the stone its name — apparently because it was first discovered by the river Achates (now called Dirillo) in southern Sicily.

As agate is so conspicuous and brightly coloured, it is understandable that it was one of the earliest stones to be noticed. It was widely used by the ancient Sumerians and Egyptians. Practically every culture of ancient times used agate not only for ornamental purposes and for making a variety of vessels, but also for making all sorts of amulets. The famous cameos and gems were carved from agate and so were beautifully engraved decorative articles, which were highly valued. Agates are most suitable for this purpose, for their variance of colour and unrepeatable pattern ensure originality when used as a precious stone. The earliest agate gems usually represented various symbols. As the occurrence of these most beautiful natural stones is so very rare, it is no wonder that their presence was considered something extraordinary, and even that it was caused by supernatural powers.

As the standard of working the agates was very high in ancient Greece, articles made from them caught the attention of the rest of the world. This raw material was turned into the most magnificent works of art. The names of the Greek artists (for example, Diodoras of Samos, Semon, Daidalos and others) have survived down the ages. The most famous was Pyrgoteles, the stone engraver of Alexander the Great; ancient and modern forgers have copied his monogram. Apart from such perfect works of art, less demanding articles, such as seals and ornaments, were made from this mineral.

101 Agate — Kozákov (Czech Republic); actual size 10,5 x 7,5 cm

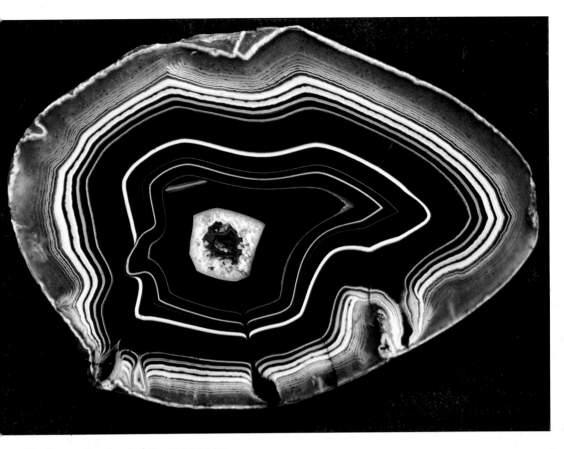

102 Onyx — Brazil; actual size 10.5 x 7.5 cm

The Romans, inheritors of the Greek culture, soon learned the art of working agates, especially how to make the traditional cut seal rings. They also gained a great deal of knowledge from the cultures of Asia and Africa, with which they had regular contact. The oldest Roman agate gems, formed as scarabs, are a proof of this. Agate rings were worn in Rome from very early days. But originally only Roman patricians were permitted to wear them. Hannibal, after his victorious battle at Cannae (216 BC), where he defeated the Roman legions, was able to determine the number of killed Roman leaders and their rank from their rings bearing rank insignia; he sent the agate rings to Carthage as a war trophy. In about 85 BC the very first collection of agate gems was founded in Rome, the so-called Dactyliotheca. But a much more valuable collection of far greater beauty was based on the war spoils from the battles between Pompey and Mithridates. In 61 BC it was exhibited at the Capitol as a thanksgiving to the gods for victory.

After the fall of the Roman Empire, the traditional art of working the agate moved east to Byzantium (Constantinople). However, the exquisite works of this era, engraved in agate, must be attributed mainly to Greek artists. The art of colouring agates black or red by heating was very popular and was a speciality of craftsmen in Constantinople. These methods were kept secret within the stone engravers' circles and were passed from generation to generation through many centuries. Even today we do not know some of the processes used by the artists of that era. After the fall of Constantinople and the Turkish occupation, the glyptic art went into decline, and so did the popularity of agates, once the most sought-after stones.

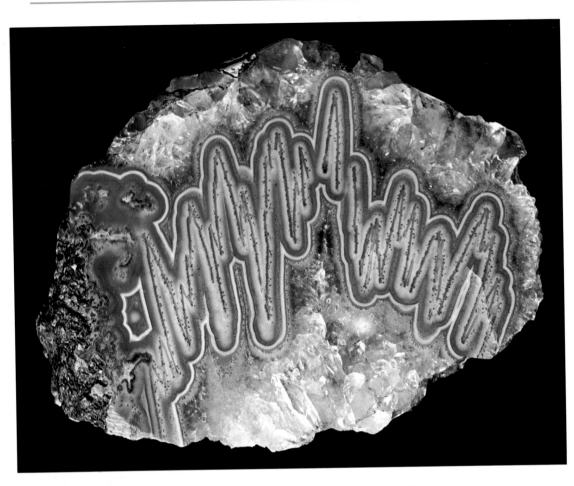

103   Agate — Horní Halže, near Měděnec (Czech Republic); actual size 12 x 9.5 cm

Agates usually occur in amygdaloidal holes of melaphyres and similar rocks. Such rocks have originated through volcanic activity which culminated in the spilling of hot bubbly lava, rich in gases, over the soil surface. After the gases escaped from the lava, the numerous crevices and cavities were filled with concentrically arranged concre-tions of agates formed by the cooling of the hot solutions in them. These fillers, much harder and more resilient than the rock itself, also occur in the topsoil when it is formed by weathering of the original rock. The agate layers are usually gaily coloured and as a rule the individual bands mirror the shape of the cavity in which the original siliceous solution precipitated. The systematically arranged bands are clearly visible once the agate is cut and polished; in fact sometimes the opening through which the solutions and all the colouring additions entered, is also distinguishable. In the centre of agates which have not been completely filled, crystals of rock quartz, smoky quartz or ame-thysts frequently occur.

Some agates are finely porous and so can be artificially coloured. Brazilian agates are highly suitable for this, because the porosity of their individual layers differs greatly: the less porous layers do not take colour and remain white or naturally pale. This variation was recognised early and stone engravers in Constantinople already knew how to colour agate by artificial means. Today inorganic dyes are mostly used in adding colouring to agates.

The most noted agate deposits are in Brazil, especially in the state of Rio Grande do Sul near the Uruguay border. Agates found at Kathiavar, India, in China, in the Urals, Siberia and Iceland are not of such a high quality. The best European deposits are in Germany at Idar-Oberstein in the Rhineland and in Saxony (mainly at Schlottwitz) and also in Romania.

During the 14th century, agates were recovered mainly from numerous sites in Saxony, and during the 16th and 17th centuries from the foothill areas on the Czech side of the Riesengebirge (Giant Mountains). They were particularly popular in the reign of Emperor Rudolf II who commissioned collectors to pick the stones for him. In the 19th century the largest deposits were in the Rhineland and the stones were worked at Idar-Oberstein; these workshops in fact became the core from which the world gemstone-working industry has grown.

Although agate is not as popular now as it used to be, it is still used for the manufacture of art objects, dishes, goblets, boxes, writing sets, paperweights, ashtrays and other things. Seal rings are still popular, especially those made from onyx and carneolonyx (sardonyx). Like chalcedony, agate is also widely used in various branches of industry.

104 Agate of the ruins — Schlottwitz, Saxony (Germany); actual size of detail 5 x 5 cm

Opal - *hydrous silicon dioxide*, $SiO_2 \cdot nH_2O$

Amorphous; H. 5.5–6.5; Sp. gr. 1.9–2.3 g/cm³; colourless, white, yellow-red (fire opal), rarely differently coloured; precious opal displays opalescence in various shades of different colours, usually white, red and blue; waxy, greasy or pearly lustre; S. white to colourless

Because of its striking colours, opal was one of the first precious stones to be used for ornamental purposes and it was highly valued even in ancient times. The earliest extant objects made of opal date back to approximately 500 BC.

Its name is from an old Latin term *opalus* used by Pliny the Elder, at first for only the precious opal. Pliny writes: 'The flat precious stone called opalus is the most valuable of all stones, but it is difficult to define it and describe it. It has the gentler fire of the ruby, the brilliant purple of the amethyst and the sea-green of the emerald, all shining together in an indescribable union'.

It is said that the Roman senator Nonius, who was the owner of a fine and valuable engraved opal, chose exile rather than surrender the stone, which was no bigger than a hazelnut, to the great commander, triumvir Marcus Antonius (AD 121–180).

The popularity of opals, especially the precious variety with an exceptional play of colour, has lasted through the ages and continues today. The most famous historical opal was the so-called Trojan Fire from the French crown jewels, which belonged to the French Empress Josephine. Today it is held in the collections of the Natural History Museum in Paris.

Opal always forms amorphous globose stones of bunchy, stalactite or reniform shapes. Frequently it fills cavities in rocks. It also occurs in veins and bands, or rarely

105   Precious opal — Barraco River, Queensland (Australia); actual size 10 x 9.5 cm

106   Precious opal — Dubník (Slovakia); actual size 9 x 6 cm

as pseudomorphs after other minerals. The colour differs according to the variety. The content of water, which is not constant, has a great influence on the play of colours. There is usually 3 to 13 per cent water in opals, but some opals may contain as much as 34 per cent water while others may have a neglible amount.

Precious opal is outstanding among all the precious stones for it has the most perfect, brilliant iridescent play of colours. This is caused by the diffusion and refraction of light rays when they meet the regularly distributed tiny balls of amorphous silicon dioxide (as has recently been proved with an electron microscope). This is often enhanced by the finely scattered foreign particles or minute cavities filled with water. When expertly treated, this optical characteristic of opal can be emphasised even more. Opal is therefore considered as one of the most valuable precious stones, though it has the lowest hardness of them all (only 5 to 6.5 on the Mohs scale). In spite of this deficiency, which would have been unforgivable in other stones, opal rouses great enthusiasm among collectors.

Black opal is the most valuable of all opals; it is a dark variety of precious opal with intensive colour change, and was first found late in the 19th century in Australia. For some time, black opal was valued as highly as diamond. Fire opal is the most beautiful opal variety; it is richly red, like a hyacinth, and transparent, with excellent opalescence, especially after being polished. Its colouring varies between light brown-yellow and rich brownish-red. The stone was brought to Europe from Mexico by the German natural historian Alexander von Humboldt (1769–1859), who had found it when studying the activity of volcanoes in Mexico.

Hydrophane is mineralogically most interesting. It is a precious opal which, when exposed to air, loses water and therefore also its characteristic play of colours. When immersed in water, the play of colours returns. From the jeweller's point of view, valuing such a stone is problematical.

The play of colours is characteristic of only some of the varieties of opal. For example, hyalite, also called glassy opal (the clearest, purest opal) is completely clear. The most widely known variety is semi-opal, which is compact, non-transparent to translucent, and occurs in various, often bright, colours. Semi-opal (also called common opal) has different names according to its colouring.

Milk opal is milky white in colour and is a mixture of opal and crystalline aggregates of silicon dioxide, recognisable only under the microscope. Milk opal faces are usually translucent.

The colouring of opals is caused by the presence of oxides of various metals, usually iron (wax opal, for example) and also by the presence (inclusions) of foreign bodies. Serpentine opal belongs to this group; green in colour, it contains a multitude of tiny serpentine particles and was formed through the decomposition of serpentine. Forcherite is orange-yellow, coloured by orpiment, and is found in cracks of gneisses at Knittelfeld in Styria (Austria). The very similar yellow-brown fiorite forms reniform concretions in trachyte cracks at Santa Fiora in Tuscany in northern Italy. Jaspopals are richly and gaily coloured mixtures of opal and chalcedony, microcrystalline quartz and mineral pigments. Prasopal is coloured green by aqueous nickel metasilicates. It is found at Kozmice in the Polish part of Silesia and also occurs in New Caledonia in the South Pacific.

Menilite (named after the Ménil Montant deposit in Paris) are distinctly layered grey-brown opal concretions, resembling flint. Cacholong is a chalky white mixture of opal with chalcedony. Wood opal is formed from opal matter penetrating through wood

107 Fire opal — Zimapan (Mexico); actual size 9 x 7.5 cm

but retaining wood structure. One of its varieties is tabasheer, permeated into bamboo stalks.

Opal is by no means as abundant under natural conditions as quartz. It occurs through deposition from hot solutions, for example from hot springs (geyserite), or through the decomposition of silicates in rocks, especially in serpentinites. It may also develop in a similar way in andesites and basalts. Opal rocks, tripolites (polishing or diatom slates), named after occurrences in the Tripoli region (Libya), originated from deposits of many minute silicified skeletons of the diatom algae. They are usually earthy in appearance. If they are of a loose consistency, they are called diatomaceous earth, or infusorial earth (the name is incorrect, but earlier natural scientists thought that this material was composed of the skeletons of infusorians). Menilite and cacholong are, for the most part, of organic origin. They occur therefore in sedimentary rocks. Opal can also be found in sandstones.

Diatom slates are used for the polishing of metals, in the manufacture of dynamite, as a heat and sound insulator and in filtering chemicals. Geyserite is used in the manufacture of some ceramic products, such as special enamels.

The oldest deposits of precious opal are at Dubník near Prešov in Slovakia, known all over the world for its 'Hungarian opal'. Apparently the deposit was known in ancient times, and many of the world's best-known precious opals were recovered there, including the 'Trojan fire' mentioned earlier. Precious opal occurs in these deposits in the cracks and crevices of andesite rocks, especially breccias and tuff. It is particularly noticeable for the beautiful, soft play of colours — violet-blue, blue-green and red hues. The volcanic rocks from the Tertiary period and their tuffs, especially the andesite and trachyte ranges of central and southern Slovakia, yield a wealth of deposits of common opals. The largest and the most beautiful opal preserved to this day was found in the bed of a stream at Dubník in 1775. Today it is in the collection of the Natural Science Museum in Vienna. It weighs approximately 600 g, and measures 12.5 x 5.7 cm. Eighty years ago it was valued at 700,000 ducats. The largest collection of opals from the Dubník deposits is in the Natural Science Museum in Budapest. The discovery of Australian and later Mexican opals of more vivid colours brought the glory of the Slovakia opals to an end.

The richest contemporary deposits of opals are in Australia: in New South Wales, Victoria and Queensland. The deposits were discovered in the second half of the 19th

century. An interesting tale is spread about the discovery. According to the story, a hunter shot a kangaroo in the outback; the animal fell to the ground but kicked the earth with such force that soil flew to all sides. Suddenly the soil glowed with vivid colours. The hunter filled his pockets with chippings of a strange stone. In Adelaide he showed them to a goldsmith, who immediately recognised that they were the precious opal. He bought up all the pieces — and this was the start of 'opal fever'. The outback filled with hopeful opal searchers, and they founded the small town of White Cliffs, north-east of Broken Hill (NSW). According to historical sources, Australian opals were first recovered in 1875.

In the Australian deposits precious opals occur in many varied forms. The stones which stand out with their exceptionally intensive play of colours are called 'harlequins'. The most valuable black opal occurs only in the deposit at White Cliffs. Opal mining is of great economic significance in Australia.

The biggest uncut Australian opal, 50 x 15 cm in size, is in the possession of the Natural Science Museum in New York. The biggest cut and polished Australian opal is at the Smithsonian Institution, Washington, and weighs 155 carats. Towards the end of the 19th century, yet another outstanding stone was discovered in Queensland; while it was being recovered, it split in half. One piece is now among the royal treasures of Britain and weighs 250 carats. It has a wondrous play of colours, including scarlet, am-ethyst-violet, dark green and purple shades. There are other deposits of precious opal in Virgin Valley, Nevada, and also in Mexico.

Beautiful fire opals have been recovered since 1870 in the surroundings of Zimapan in northern Mexico. They occur in cracks and crevices of porphyritic trachyte. Similar fire opals occur in Asia Minor but they have not as yet been extensively mined. In India there are many occurrences of different varieties of common opal (dendrites). Wood opal occurs in the state of Idaho, USA, where beautiful trunks of oak are found permeated with opal in the Clover Creek deposits. The now exhausted deposits of hyalite in the basalt rocks of Valeč in the Doupovské Hills (Czech Republic), are well known. Larger hyalite deposits are at St. Luis Potosí in Mexico. Hyalite in the interesting form of tiny spheres occurs in Japan. Their formation is an after-effect of volcanic action, when hot solutions permeated the cracks and crevices of rocks, leaching silicon dioxide and depositing grape-like clusters of unusual beauty in cooler places near the surface.

Apart from Ménil Montant (Paris), menilite also occurs in western part of the Czech Republic. Cacholong occurs in Mongolia. Opal's variety, geyserite, forms from deposits around hot springs in Iceland and in the Yellowstone National Park in the USA.

Opals which have an attractive play of colours are much sought after. Semi-opals, too, are often used for ornamental purposes. Dendritic opals are most suitable for this. Cutting and polishing enhances and magnifies their branching, interwoven patterns. Wood opals are also suitable.

Most opals are given the cabochon cut; the cut with facets is applied only exceptionally (to fire opals of the highest quality, for instance). When cutting precious opal, or fire opal, more attention is paid to enhancing their iridescence than to the shape of the actual cut.

In 1921, the art of colouring opals by synthetic means was discovered completely by chance. Bittner-Belangenay, a Frenchman who had a licence to exploit the Dubník deposit, happened to spill ink on a few opals on his table. The ink coloured some of the stones so perfectly that even when completely dry, and even after washing and cutting, they shone with unusual, unknown colours and hues. Opals coloured by such artificial means were given the name 'chameleon'.

It was believed in ancient times that an opal brought its owner good luck; it is therefore difficult to explain the modern superstition that this beautiful and popular stone brings bad fortune. It is said the rumour was spread by the owners of the opal mines at Dubník in an effort to stop the extensive stealing of opal in the 1870s. It seems they were partially successful.

◁
109 Hyalite — San Louis Potosí (Mexico); actual size of globose aggregates up to 3.5 cm

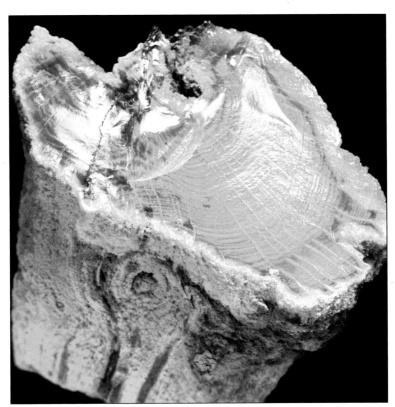

110 Wood opal — Clover Creek, Idaho (USA); actual size 15 x 9 cm

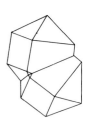

111 Cassiterite –
Bolivia; actual size
of crystal 6 cm

Cassiterite - *tin dioxide*, SnO_2

Tetragonal; H. 6–7; Sp.gr. 6.8–7.1 g/cm^3; brown to black, more rarely yellow to reddish; adamantine to metallic lustre; S. pale brown to white

Cassiterite has served humans well as tin ore from ancient times, for it can be easily worked and extracted. Humans had already learned to smelt it by the 6th millenium BC, before they knew how to smelt iron. Cassiterite was heated with charcoal in simple clay or stone kilns, where a temperature of 1000°C could be reached, and produced tin. As copper ores were often present with cassiterite and they were all melted together, an extremely hard yellow alloy of tin and copper frequently resulted. This is how humans first came to manufacture bronze, a metal of far superior quality, compared to the soft tin. Many useful objects were made from bronze.

Cassiterite sometimes forms perfect columnar crystals, often twinned. More often it is massive, granular, or in the form of fibrous aggregates. Sometimes it is disseminated in rocks (greisen), or it forms lodes, often in asssociation with copper, tungsten and molybdenum ores. It is also recovered from alluvial placers. The largest alluvial deposits are in Malaysia (Kuala Lumpur), which yield one-third of the world's production, and in Indonesia (Bangka and Belitung islands). The largest primary deposits are in Bolivia. In Europe the chief primary deposits are in Cornwall (UK), in Brittany (France) and in the Erzgebirge (Ore Mountains) in the Czech Republic.

Cassiterite happens to be almost the only ore of tin. However, it is a very rich ore, containing up to 78.6 per cent tin, and occurs in considerable amounts at some deposits; the remaining tin ores do not carry such a high content of metal and, as a rule, do not occur in sufficient quantities to warrant mining. It is therefore not surprising that the mining of cassiterite is on the rise in all deposits. Tin is used chiefly in food packaging (cans, tin foils) because it is safe for human health.

Cassiterite is a popular mineral with collectors. In particular its crystals, which usually occur as twins or multiples (up to ninefold) are highly prized. Most of the large crystals, held in collectors' and world museums' collections, come from the greisen deposits of Modot in Mongolia and Oulmés in Morocco (crystals up to 15 cm in size).

Rutile - *titanium dioxide*, TiO_2

Tetragonal; H. 6; Sp.gr. 4.2–4.3 g/cm³; brown-red, scarlet, more rarely yellow-brown, also black (nigrine); vitreous to adamantine lustre, nigrine submetallic; S. pale brown to yellowish, grey-black to green-black

Rutile has been found in many alluvial placers and in quartz veins in the form of columnar crystals. Because of its appearance, it was often taken for tourmaline. In 1795 the German chemist M. Klaproth found the mineral contained a substantial amount of titanium. The present name was suggested in 1801 by Abraham Gottlob Werner, a German mineralogist and geologist; it comes from the Latin *rutilus* ('golden yellow', 'reddish-yellow', 'ginger'). No one visualised in those days how important rutile would be as a titanium ore.

Long before this, rutile was known in a completely different form. There were many places in the Alps where magnificent clear quartz was found, containing slender, needle-like, often thickly interwoven crystals; they often formed an unusual, interesting type of netting and helped to enhance the otherwise rather uniform mineral. They were given the name 'sagenite' and were thought at first to be a separate mineral. They were widely used as decorative stones for rings and necklaces, and were often called

112 Sagenite in rock crystal — Modriach (Austria); actual size 3 x 3 cm

113   Rutile — Alps; actual size of larger twin 13 mm

'the hair of Venus' or 'arrows of love' (*fléches d'amour*). That the mineral was rutile was established only much later.

The columnar crystals of rutile are often twinned in the form of geniculate twins, or complex multiple twins. Rutile often occurs as cobbles, or in granular or acicular form. Rutile's jet-black variety, rich in iron, is called nigrine. This variety is abundant in schists, in some igneous rocks lacking in silicon dioxides, in syenites and diorites, and in quartz veins of gneisses and mica schists. As it is resistant to weathering, rutile also occurs in some alluvials. There are some magnificent rutile crystals in Modriach in Styria; sagenites are recovered from the Tirol and there are rutile deposits in Switzerland (St. Gotthard), Czech Republic (near Soběslav) and southern Norway (the Krageroe deposit is particularly rich in rutile crystals), as well as in Russia (the Ilmen range of the Urals), in many places in the USA (Arkansas and Georgia, where, in Lincoln county, perfect crystals up to 15 cm in size, with numerous faces, are found). Attractive crystals are also found in Brazil. Rutile is a substantial source of titanium, which is used in the aerospace and other high-technology industries. With iron, rutile forms an alloy, ferrotitanium, which improves the quality of steel, especially its resistance to corrosion and heat, and raises weldability. Titanium white and other alloys are all well known. It is also employed for some abrasive materials. Rutile contains 61.1 per cent titanium.

Natural rutiles are used only rarely as precious gems. Then they are usually cut in the brilliant or cabochon cut, which makes the most of the high lustre. Synthetic rutile is one of the most beautiful artificial precious stones. In contrast to the natural stone, it is transparent and its hardness is low.

Anatase - *titanium dioxide*, TiO_2

Tetragonal; H. 5.5–6; S.p. gr. 3.90 g/cm^3; blue-grey, black, brown, yellow, often zonated; adamantine to metallic lustre; S. colourless to pale yellow

Anatase was given the name from the Greek *anatasis* ('elongation'), because of the crystal form. It shares rutile's chemical composition and crystal symmetry, but has a different internal structure. The usual form of anatase crystals is of steep double pyramids with a particularly strong lustre. Anatase is far rarer than rutile. Most frequently it occurs in druses of metamorphic rocks in veins of Alpine paragenesis. Brookite is often its associate in the cracks of gneisses. The traditional deposits of anatase are in the Alps (particularly the Swiss mountains). New discoveries are constantly being made in the Tavetsch, Binn and Maderan valleys and at St. Gotthard, and also at Le Bourg d'Oisans in France, at the Rauris deposit in Austria and at some of the deposits in the Italian Alps. Well known deposits are in the environs of Kutná Hora in the Czech Republic, at Minas Gerais in Brazil, and in the Urals (Russia).

Anatase has no industrial significance, but is sought after by collectors. The transparent crystals of gem quality, found in the diamond-bearing gravels Minas Gerais in Brazil, are particularly valued. Beautiful blue anatase crystals have been recently discovered in diorites at Beaver Creek (Gunnison county), Colorado, and at Bothaville in the Orange Free State (South Africa).

114   Anatase
— Sonnblick
(Austria);
actuals size
of crystals
12 x 9 mm

Brookite - *titanium dioxide*, TiO_2

Orthorhombic; H. 5.5–6; Sp. gr. 4.14 g/cm³; yellow-brown to black; adamantine to metallic lustre; S. colourless

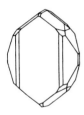

Brookite was so named in honour of the British crystallographer and mineralogist, H. J. Brook (1771–1857). It shares the chemical composition of the two preceding minerals, but in contrast to them it crystallises in orthorhombic form. It always occurs as crystals, which are usually small and tabular. On rare occasions it occurs in cracks of gneisses, and even more rarely is found in druse hollows in pegmatites (especially those of the albite type) and other rocks. Like anatase, brookite has no industrial significance but is much sought after by collectors. Main deposits are at St. Gotthard and in the Maderaner Tall in Switzerland, where it is possible to find beautiful brown tabular crystals up to 5 cm in size, at Prägraten in Tirol (Austria) and at Miass in the Urals. Pseudohexagonal pyramidal crystals (arkansite variety) are found in Magnet Cave in Arkansas; they are commonly embedded in cloudy grey columns of quartz.

115 Brookite — Amsteg (Switzerland); actual size of crystals 6–14 mm

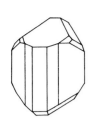

116 Wolframite
— Horní Slavkov
(Czech Republic);
actual size of
crystals 1.5 cm

Wolframite - *oxide of tungsten and manganese with iron* (Mn,Fe)WO$_4$

Monoclinic; H. 4.5–5.5; Sp. gr. 7–7.5 h/cm^3; iron black with a brownish shade; submetallic lustre; S. black

Wolframite was once considered an unwelcome admixture in smelting tin ores. Apparently wolframite was given its name by old German miners, since during the process of melting it 'gnawed' (like a wolf) through cassiterite. The element wolfram, discovered in 1781, was named after wolframite. It is now more often called tungsten. For a long time tungsten was considered a valueless gangue material, though today it is sought after. According to the old grouping system, wolframite was thought to be wolframate (tungstate) and was placed in the group of sulphates and similar compounds. Its classification as an oxide is of a comparatively recent date. Columnar to tabular crystals or crystals of perfect cleavage, and scaly or fibrous aggregates of wolframite, usually occur in cassiterite veins, which they frequently dominate. The most important deposits are in the USA (Boulder county in Colorado), in Bolivia and in South Korea; in Europe the largest deposits are in Portugal (Panasqueira), in the Clara mine near Oberwolfach in Germany and in the Erzgebirge (Ore Mountains) in the Czech Republic.

Tungsten is predominantly used in the steel industry in the manufacture of steels for high-speed cutting tools and for the manufacture of filaments of electric bulbs, which often are as thin as 0.01 mm. These uses depend on the exceptionally high melting point of tungsten (3,390°C — the highest of all metals). Many compounds of tungsten are excellent dyes and are also used for impregnation purposes in fire-proofing cloth. Compounds of tungsten are also widely employed in a number of other branches of industry. Wolframite is the most important ore of tungsten. Similar to wolframite is the rare tantalite — oxide of tantalum and iron with niobium and manganese (Fe,Mn)(Ta,Nb)$_2$O$_6$, forming orthorhombic crystals. Tantalite is practically the only source of tantalum and is used in the production of chemical equipment, parts of surgical instruments and nozzles used in the manufacture of synthetic fibres.

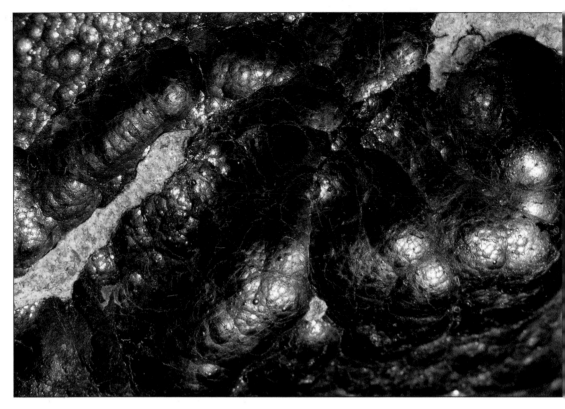

117   Uraninite — Jáchymov (Czech Republic); actual size of detail 37 x 27 mm

Uraninite - *uranium dioxide with thorium* $(U,Th)O_2$

Cubic; H. 5–6; Sp. gr. 8–10 g/cm^3; black with shades of green, brownish or grey; resinous to greasy lustre; S. brownish-black, greyish to olive green

Uraninite was mined in Jáchymov (Czech Republic) in fairly substantial quantities probably from the onset of silver mining, and was at first thought to be an ore with a small admixture of silver. Later it was proved that there was no silver present. This mineral, which closely resembles pitch, was called pitchblende and because it seemed to have no use, it was thrown away with other gangue. Today it is difficult to comprehend how this most valuable ore of such important uranium and radium compounds could have been discarded as useless material.

In 1787, M. Klaproth, a German chemist, discovered a new metal in the pitchblende, and he named it uranium, after the newly discovered planet Uranus. In 1852 the Czech metallurgist A. Patera began to manufacture bright uranium dyes from the pitchblende.

Uraninite was the first mineral to be found to emit a special radiation. The phenomenon, now known as radioactivity, was discovered in 1896 by the French physicist Henri Becquerel. Shortly afterwards, Marie Curie discovered in uraninite the elements radium and polonium, which emit more radiation than uranium. Both Becquerel and Marie Curie used uraninite from Jáchymov for their experiments. The Austro-Hungarian government gave permission, considering it a material of no practical value.

Uraninite usually forms compact vein fillings, less often reniform aggregates. Crystal form is rare (for example, in Norway and Sweden). It occurs in ore veins, in pegmatites, granites and coals. Uraninite is not a constant mineral. All too often many secondary minerals form from its alternation, including oxides, carbonates, phosphates and silicates, which have vividly bright colours (yellow, green, orange and others). The surface layers of uraninite veins, accessible to water and oxygen, are particularly rich in radioactive elements. Uraninite is distinct for its high density. The radioactivity of uraninite is very strong. If placed with the ground surface on a photographic plate, a natural image of uraninite (a radiogram) will form through the emanation of disintegrated particles of the radioactive elements.

The largest uraninite deposits are in Canada, north of Lake Huron, and in Zaire (Chingolobwe in Katanga). This is where big but imperfectly bounded crystals of uraninite occur, with faces up to 4 cm long. Even larger crystals are found in the locality of Wilberforce (Renfrew county) in Ontario, Canada. They are shaped either like a cube or an imperfect dodecahedron, and are up to 10 cm in size. In all these deposits, uraninite occurs in the vicinity of granite massifs.

Uraninite, which contains 75 to 96 per cent uranium, and some radium and polonium, is today the principal ore of these radioactive elements, on which the interest of the world is centred. It is a source of nuclear energy and as such it has become a most important strategic material. There are such negligible traces of radium in uraninite (radium is used in medicine) that from a whole wagonload of uraninite less than 1 g of radium can be recovered.

Goethite - *hydrous iron oxide*, FeO(OH)

Orthorhombic; H. 5–5.5; Sp. gr. 4.3 g/cm³ (in aggregates it falls to 3.3); black-brown, red-brown; adamantine to metallic lustre; S. brownish-yellow to orange-yellow

Goethite was often found in the cavities of limonite and taken for one of its varieties. In 1806 it was identified as a separate mineral, and named goethite in honour of the great German poet and dramatist Goethe (1749–1832), who was also a collector of

118   Goethite, velvet variety — Příbram (Czech Republic); actual size of detail 16 x 11 cm

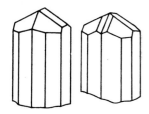

minerals. In colour and chemical composition it resembles limonite. However, in contrast to limonite, it forms small crystals which are usually fine and needle-shaped. The rusty brown colour and velvety smoothness of the crystals are typical of the 'velvet variety' found in Příbram (Czech Republic). Goethite occurs with limonite through the weathering of pyrite, or may be formed from hot solutions (hydrothermal origin), or by dehydration of limonite. The most noted deposits are in Siegerland (Germany) and in Cornwall (UK). In the Slovakian Erzgebirge (Ore Mountains) it is mined as an iron ore from deposits in which it is present in larger quantities simultaneously with limonite. Economically it is of little value. Large pseudomorphs after pyrite are found at Pelican Point near Great Salt Lake in Utah (USA).

Limonite - *hydrous iron oxide*, $FeO(OH)+nH_2O$

Colloidal; H. variable, typically 4–5.5; Sp. gr. 2.7–4.3 g/cm³; brown to yellow; vitreous to dull lustre; S. brown

Limonite is in fact natural rust. It is common in occurrence and originates mostly through the weathering of other iron ores, whose surfaces it covers with characteristic brown stains; old miners in some countries called it 'iron cap'. Limonite is usually powdery or earthy, but also compact, with a reniform to stalactitic surface. From haematite, with which it often occurs, it is distinguishable by the conspicuous colour of its streak. The most noted deposits are in Sweden and Finland, where it is called 'bog-iron ore' or 'lake ore', since it is found on the beds of some lakes. The action of micro-organisms is involved in the formation of these ores.

119 Limonite — Rožňava (Slovakia); actual size 13 x 8 cm

As the content of iron in the ore is comparatively low, it pays to recover limonite only where it is found in large quantities or when it is associated with other iron ores. Mineralogically interesting deposits of limonite are in Slovakia. The largest 'iron cap' (gosan) developed through the oxidation of large deposits of pyrite in Rio Tinto, Spain. The earthy and powdery varieties are called ochres or clays; the compact, lump varieties, with a resinous lustre, are called stilpnosiderite (from the Greek *stilpnos*, 'glossy', and *sideros*, 'iron').

Manganite - *hydrous manganese oxide*, MnO(OH)

Monoclinic; H. 4; Sp. gr. 4.33 g/cm³; steel grey to black; submetallic lustre; S. red-brown to black

Manganite was known in ancient times and was used in the decolorisation of glass, according to ancient historians. The yellowish colour of the crude vitreous matter was aptly balanced by the gentle violet colour of manganese compounds which were added. At first manganese compounds were not distinguished from iron ores, which are similar, but in the second half of the 18th century their difference was recognised. Manganite is usually found in association with pyrolusite (manganese dioxide) and psilomelane (complex massive oxide of manganese, usually with some barium), often in deposits with admixtures of iron oxides. Every famous collection in the world contains druses of columnar crystals of manganite from Ilfeld in the Harz mountains, Germany.

Manganite is one of the most important ores of manganese, containing 60 per cent metal. Manganese is added to steel to improve its elasticity, compactness and resistance to impact. Manganese is also used in the chemical industry for the manufacture of disinfectants, dyes, batteries and matches.

120 Manganite — Ilfeld, Harz mountains (Germany); actual size of crystals 15 mm

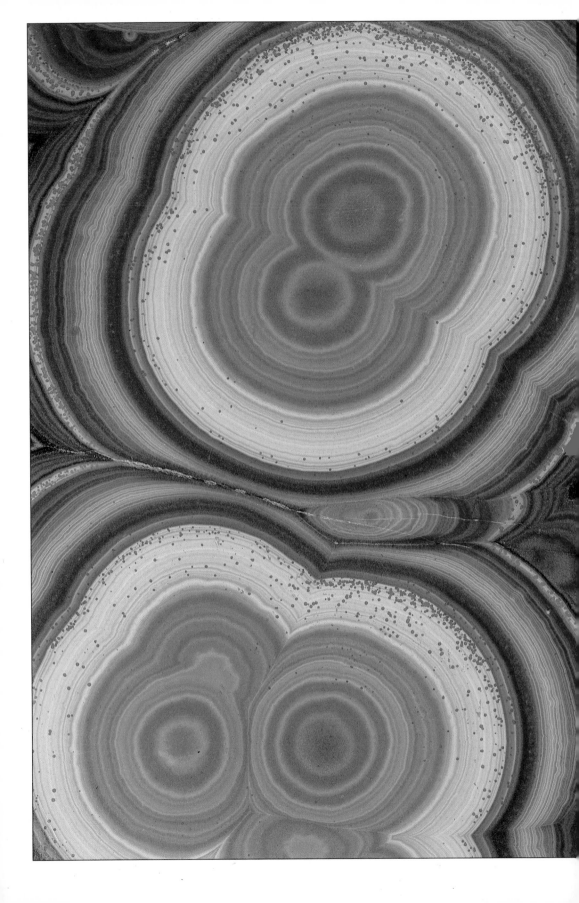

Chapter 5

CARBONATES

Carbonates are a large and important group of salts deriving from carbonic acid. Their origin is varied and their occurrence is governed by the fact that they are substances with very little resistance to acids and that they decompose at high temperatures under comparatively low pressure.

They are divided into anhydrous, hydrous or alkaline. The anhydrous carbonates fall almost entirely into large groups, called isomorph series, whose members have the same internal structure and can intermingle. Thus, there are, for example, the calcite series with rhombohedral crystallisation (calcite, magnesite, siderite, rhodochrosite, smithsonite and other, rarer carbonates) and the aragonite series with orthorhombic crystallisation (aragonite, cerussite and others). Double salts (for example, dolomite and similar ankerite with Ca, Fe and Mn), which also show rhombohedral, though slightly different, crystallisation, are closely allied to the calcite series. The hydrous carbonates and alkaline carbonates (there is not always a clear border between these two series) contain chiefly carbonates of bivalent metals such as copper, lead, zinc and others.

Natural occurrences of nitrates and borates are commonly included with carbonates because they have some properties in common. Nitrates include, for example, the orthorhombic saltpeter, which is chemically potassium nitrate, KNO_3, and the rhombohedral niter, or Chile saltpeter (sodium nitrate, $NaNO_3$). Of the borates, two are of technical importance: monoclinic borax, which is chemically hydrous sodium tetraborate, $Na_2B_4O_7.10H_2O$; and kernite, also a monoclinic sodium tetraborate, $Na_2B_4O_7.4H_2O$.

Calcite - *calcium carbonate*, $CaCO_3$

Rhombohedral, H. 3; Sp. gr. 2.6–2.8 g/cm³; commonly colourless, white, brownish, yellow, blue, and of other shades (see text), but rarely dark; vitreous lustre, pearly on cleavage surfaces; S. white

Calcite aroused no interest until the second half of the 17th century, when a very strange discovery was made on the Helgustadir farm near Eskifjord, on the eastern coast of Iceland. While extracting basalt, stone workers hit a cavity 6 x 3 m in size, which was filled with a multitude of grey-white spindly calcite crystals. Many of them were clear, others only partially. The recovered calcite excited attention by its shape and colouring and, as a so-called 'silverstone', was exported to Europe.

Erasmus Bartholinus, a Danish surgeon, examined the mineral carefully and published his findings in 1669. He wrote of his discovery that there is a pronounced double refraction when light passes through this mineral. If we cut out a rhombohedron from a clear calcite crystal, and look at some writing through it, the words appear twice. The discovery of double refraction proved valuable in optical research.

Rocks formed by calcite — limestones — were, of course, known a long time ago. Marble (cristalline limestone) was the main material used by ancient Greek sculptors. It was extracted mainly from Paros and the mountain of Pendelikon near Athens. Many magnificent works of ancient Greek and Roman art made of marble can be admired even today. Just as Greece used to be, Italy was and still is renowned for its marble. During the 15th century, extensive mining for marble began on the slopes of the Apennines, especially near Carrara. In the Middle Ages marble was used mainly to decorate churches and for sculpture. The so-called 'marble of the ruins' from Florence was also very popular at that time.

122 Calcite —
Helgustadir
(Iceland); actual
size 30 x 15 cm

Apart from quartz, calcite is the most common mineral and occurs in an almost endless variety of form. Crystallographers have identified more than 500 different calcite crystal shapes and over 1500 combinations. Calcite crystals are usually rhombohedra, both low and high, which have perfect cleavage and as a rule are grouped in shapely druses. However, there are also columnar, thin to thick tabular, scalenohedral and even pyramidal calcite crystals. The crystals are often variously twinned.

Because calcite is readily soluble, it is often replaced by other materials, forming pseudomorphs after calcite; most commonly such pseudomorphs are formed by quartz, chalcedony, limonite, gypsum and other minerals. On the other hand, calcite itself forms pseudomorphs after aragonite, barytes, fluorite, quartz, gypsum, anhydrite and others.

If pure, calcite is colourless to white; however, under natural conditions it is usually coloured, deepening in the presence of various phenocrysts and isomorph admixtures. For example, pink calcites usually contain more manganese, and purple-violet calcites have more cobalt. The origin of some colour shades (for example, some blue marbles) still needs clear explanation. Many calcites intensively luminesce under ultraviolet light. Granular calcites from some sites of the Příbram deposit (Vrančice) contain lead and manganese and have a very attractive red luminiscence; local people call them 'fright stones'.

Massive varieties produce whole rock masses which consist of coarse-grained or fine-grained to compact limestone, rarely also containing stalky to fibrous aggregates, oolites and concretions. The majority of the stalagmites and stalactites found in various deposits are composed of limestone and may have, on exceptional occasions, crystal faces at the end. All the distinctively dissimilar shapes of calcite and limestone, ranging from beautiful crystal forms — often bounded by numerous perfectly developed surfaces — to minute microscopic grains forming huge series of limestone strata of different geological age, probably resulted from the diversity of conditions during their development.

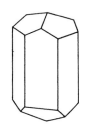

The most noted deposits of crystallised calcite are associated in ore veins. In Europe, calcite crystals occur in the lead ore deposits of northern England, particularly at Alston Moor, Egremont, Frizington and Wearsdale in Cumbria. The crystal forms most frequently found at these deposits include perfectly formed clear or reddish scalenohedra, rhombohedra or columnar crystals up to 10 cm in size, and beautiful heart-shaped twins in cavities of the veins. Deposits are also at Fontainebleau in France, in Bavaria, at Andreasberg in the Harz mountains and in Romania. The so-called 'nail-head spar', a characteristic mineral of Příbram (Czech Republic), is much sought after by collectors. It is formed by an interesting grouping of parallel twins of low rhombohedral crystals, where the upper parts resemble nail heads. Recently such crystals have also been found near Stříbro in western Bohemian region of the Czech Republic.

As to deposits outside Europe, the largest and most striking calcite crystals come from ore veins in the USA, particularly Illinois and Tennessee. The crystals found there in fluorite deposits often have a size in excess of 10 cm and are yellow to honey brown scalenohedral crystals, perfectly transparent, usually twinned. Large yellow crystals found in lead and zinc ore deposits at Joplin in Missouri are also perfectly shaped; they often grow on large crystals of galena, and some of the scalenohedra recovered at Joplin are up to 1 m in size. Ground and polished calcites from the American deposits are held in many collections. The working of these stones is difficult and their price is therefore extremely high, though they are too hard to be used for jewels. Excellent glossy calcite crystals are also to be found at Guanajuato in Mexico.

Crystallised calcite also occurs in cavities of extrusive rocks, for example in phonolite cavities on the Mariánská hill at Ústí on the Elbe (Czech Republic), in the melaphyre rocks at Idar Oberstein in Germany and in similar rocks near West Paterson and elsewhere in New Jersey (USA). They are genetically related to the calcite deposits at Helgustadir in Iceland. Much larger deposits of similar nature were in cavities of basalt rocks in Taos county in New Mexico, USA: the cleavable lumps of perfectly clear Iceland-

123   Calcite — Příbram (Czech Republic); actual size of crystals 6 mm

124   Marble of the ruins — Florence (Italy); actual size of detail 14 x 9 cm

type calcite recovered there had a size of up to 6 x 2 m and some of the blocks extracted from these deposits weighed up to 25 tonnes. Similar deposits are in Montana and California in the USA and near Chihuahua in Mexico, where cleavable green calcite was found. Large blocks characterised by double refraction are quarried at Baidar in the Crimea (Ukraine). The clear scalenohedra from the melaphyre cavities near Lake Superior (Michigan), which grow on large sheets of native copper and are up to 10 cm in size, are highly valued by collectors.

Together with aragonite, calcite develops by deposition in thermal springs where it forms porous travertine, at Tivoli near Rome, for instance. Unlike marbles, which are crystalline limestones, travertines are porous, non-metamorphosed rocks. Also of freshwater origin are the calcite balls, called pisolites, from Hammam Meskoutine in Algeria or the thermal deposits in the geysers of the Yellowstone National Park in Wyoming, USA. It is not generally known that limestone is also able to produce magmatic rocks, called carbonatites; many scientists are trying to explain the conditions necessary for their formation.

Because of their double refraction property, the clear varieties of calcite are used in optical instruments, including polarising microscopes, so important for the identification and study of minerals. Limestone rocks also have various industrial uses, so that they can be considered as an important mineral material.

Rhodochrosite - *manganese carbonate*, MnCO₃

Rhombohedral; H. 4; Sp. gr.3.3–3.6 g/cm³; commonly pink to red, nearly white, dirty grey, brownish, greenish, very rarely colourless; vitreous lustre; S. white

Rhodochrosite (from the Greek *rhodon* , 'rose' and *khrosis*, 'colour'), also called dialogite (from the Greek *dialoge,* 'choice') is most frequently found in ore veins and sedimentary deposits of pyrite and manganese ores where it commonly forms small veins with pyrite and psilomelane. Less commonly it occurs in cracks of igneous rocks, such as spilites. The crystal form is rare; rhodochrosite is usually massive, coarse- or fine-grained to compact. Sometimes it forms globose, kidney-shaped, radial, clustered or botryoidal aggregates and concretions.

The most beautiful rhodochrosite crystals, scalenohedra up to 10 cm in size, were found in the 1970s at Hotazel near Kimberley in South Africa. They are ground and polished as precious stones. Magnificent crystals of rhodochrosite come also from the Harz mountains, Freiberg (Saxony), Sacaramb and Cavnic (Romania), the western states of the USA, and Usinsk (Siberia). The beautiful compact rhodochrosites which are recovered from deposits near Capilitas in the Argentine are used as precious stones. Rhodochrosite is also extracted as a manganese ore, containing up to 42.8 per cent manganese. Commercially useful deposits occur only in the Pyrenees and near Huelva in southern Spain. Rhodochrosite is particularly suitable for the manufacture of speculum metal and ferromanganese.

125 Rhodochrosite
— Cavnic (Romania);
actual size of
aggregates 12 mm

Magnesite - *magnesium carbonate*, MgCO$_3$

Rhombohedral; H. 4–4.5; Sp. gr. 3.0 g/cm^3; white, yellowish or greyish; vitreous lustre; S. white

 Magnesite was so named because it contains magnesium, but for a long time it attracted very little attention. Some 70 years ago magnesium metal was still used solely as an ingredient of fireworks or a source of light during poor lighting conditions in photography. With the development of modern industries its uses increased and continue to do so.

Like rhodochrosite and calcite, magnesite also occurs in many varied forms, either crystalline or compact. When crystalline it is fine- to coarse-grained, outwardly very closely resembling marble. Granular magnesites occur through alterations of limestone and dolomite, though on rare occasions also by direct deposition. The compact varieties develop through decomposition of serpentinites. The latter often contain admixtures of opal and are consequently hard.

The chief European magnesite localities are in Austria (Veitsch, Loeben and Mürzzuschlag in Styria), in the southern parts of Slovakia, in Russia (Satkinsk in the southern Urals), Greece, Italy (Tuscany) ; and, outside Europe, in the USA. Magnesite is extensively and widely used. It is an important material in the building industry, and a great importance is attached to its fire-resisting property. It is used in the production of porcelain, ceramics, and also in the manufacture of quick-setting cement. Heat-resistant bricks are made from it; thoroughly fired magnesite is used for the inner refractory lining of blast furnaces.

126   Magnesite — Ratkovská Suchá (Slovakia); actual size of crystals up to 1 cm

127 Siderite — Siegen (Germany); actual size of crystals up to 2 cm

Siderite - *iron carbonate*, FeCO₃

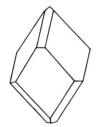

Rhombohedral; H. 4–4.5; Sp. gr. 3.7–3.9 g/cm³; commonly brown-yellow, dark brown to black, sometimes with bright metallic shades; vitreous, sometimes pearly lustre; S. white

Siderite is an important iron ore which was recovered from Erzberg mountain near Eisenerz in Austria. Erzberg, where mining still goes on today, is completely composed of siderite. Originally it was formed of limestone, but hot solutions rising from the Earth's interior simultaneously carried away and deposited matter, gradually replacing the limestone with the less soluble siderite (hydrothermal metasomatism). During this process the so-called 'iron flower', a very interesting variety of aragonite, developed from the dissolved calcium carbonate.

Siderite frequently forms veinstones or occurs in association with other ores, copper for instance. In such deposits it is massive or crystallised. The best examples of siderite's rhombohedral crystals, clustered in neat rosette-shaped formations and druses, often come from the ore veins (for example, from Neudorf in the Harz mountains). However, such occurrences are of low economic value. The occurrences of clay siderite (pelosiderite), which forms balls and nodules in some coal basins, are most interesting. They are often nearly 0.5 m long (northern England, Halle in Germany). Though containing a relatively small proportion of iron (48 per cent), siderite is an important iron ore because, compared with other iron ores, it is usually very pure and is easy to work.

128 Smithsonite — Sardinia (Italy); actual size of detail 9 x 6 cm

Smithsonite - *zinc carbonate*, $ZnCO_3$

Rhombohedral; H. 5; Sp. gr. 4.3–4.5; g/cm³; commonly grey-white, colourless, yellowish, with green or blue shades, brown; strong vitreous lustre, even slightly pearly; S. white

Smithsonite was mined very early as a zinc ore, though zinc as a metal was then unknown. How to explain this paradox? There are many beautiful brass objects extant from these days which confirm that brass (an alloy of copper and zinc) must have been produced in large quantities. Many minerals which, mixed with copper, produced the popular brass were then well known. This applies especially to so-called 'calamine' which occurs in the upper layers of zinc and lead ore veins. Not until the second half of the 18th century was it discovered that calamine was two different minerals, zinc carbonate (smithsonite) and zinc silicate (hemimorphite).

Smithsonite was named after J. Smithson (1765–1829, a British chemist and mineralogist). It forms reniform, botryoidal and bunchy aggregates or earthy crusts and fibrous clusters. As it is a product of the surface weathering of sphalerite, it occurs mainly in the upper layers of sphalerite beds. The main deposits are at Altenberg (Germany), Polish Silesia, Sardinia, Laurion (Greece) and Nerchinsk (Siberia). The most beautiful translucent compact smithsonites in existence come from the copper ores in Tsumeb in Namibia and are also used as precious and decorative stones.

Dolomite - *calcium magnesium carbonate*, $CaMg(CO_3)_2$

Rhombohedal; H. 3.5–4; Sp. gr. 2.8–2.9 g/cm³; grey, white, reddish, less commonly dark; vitreous to pearly lustre; S. white

Dolomite is one of the carbonates which resemble other carbonates so closely in various characteristics that originally they were not distinguishable. All the minerals of this appearance were therefore considered for many years as calcites and the rock as limestone. This changed in 1791, when the French geologist D.Dolomieu pointed out various different properties of a rock occurring mainly in southern Tirol in Austria. The Swiss mineralogist, H.B. de Saussure (1740–1799) studied the rock in closer detail and named it dolomite in honour of Dolomieu. With its crystal shape, chemical composition and colour, dolomite resembles calcite and magnesite. Whole mountain ranges or large areas are sometimes composed of it. Dolomitic rocks originally occurred by deposition of shells of small sea animals — their origin is similar to that of limestones. Crystallised dolomite is most commonly found in ore veins, for example at Hall (Tirol), in the Binnen valley (Switzerland), at Banská Štiavnica (Slovakia), and at Freiberg (Saxony, Germany). Outside Europe the most important deposits are in Vermont (USA) and Guanajuato (Mexico). Dolomite is used in the manufacture of special cements and for making refractory linings for blast furnaces.

129   Dolomite — Băita (Romania); actual size of crystals up to 1 cm

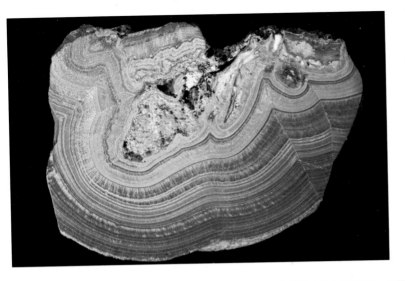

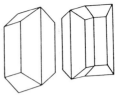

130 Sprudelstein — Karlovy Vary (Czech Republic); actual size 7 x 5 cm

Aragonite - *calcium carbonate*, $CaCO_3$

Orthorhombic; H. 3.5–4; Sp. gr. 2.95 g/cm³; usually white, grey, reddish to black; vitreous lustre; S. white

Aragonite was first discovered in the 15th century, when on Erzberg mountain near Eisenerz in northern Styria (Austria) a gallery was driven across a rich deposit of siderite ores of iron. This gallery was intended to simplify the search for silver and gold veins. The new mineral looked at first sight like a snowy white or faintly bluish plant turned to stone, and was appropriately called 'iron flower'. Basically, these are inter-twinned stalk-like aggregates.

The Swedish natural historian Linnaeus (Carl von Linné) discovered that this 'iron flower' is chemically identical to calcite. However, later experiments proved that it has a number of properties which identified it with what were supposed to be calcite crystals in Aragon (Spain). From then on the mineral was named aragonite.

131 Aragonite — Schwaz, Tyrol (Austria); actual size of aggregate 12 x 4 cm

Aragonite is distinguished from calcite in that it has a very poor cleavage and does not occur in rhombohedral form. Its columns are usually intergrown into large six-sided forms. The crystals are often acicular and fibrous. Like calcite, aragonite occurs under the most varied conditions; but calcite crystallises from comparatively cool solutions, whereas aragonite crystallises at high temperatures. This affects the inner structure, which differs from calcite and is responsible for aragonite's diverse crystal forms and physical properties.

Deposition from hot springs in Karlovy Vary in the Czech Republic gives rise to the finely layered aragonite variety, sprudelstein and the less common peastone, composed of pisolites resembling pea grains. Magnificent crystalline specimens come from Hořenec near Bílina (Czech Republic) and also from Tirol. Beautiful bushy aggregates up to several decimetres in size have recently been found at Podrečany in Slovakia; they are as popular among collectors as are crystalline specimens. The Hořenec aragonites are now worked to a facet cut — these stones have a fine yellow colour and are perfectly transparent. They serve only for collecting purposes because they are too soft to be used in jewels. The sprudelstein of Karlovy Vary, usually composed of rich brown bands of various shades, has long been used for the manufacture of ornamental objects.

Cerussite - *lead carbonate*, $PbCO_3$

Orthorhombic-pseudohexagonal; H. 3–3.5; S. gr. 6.4–6.5 g/cm³; greyish, white, greyish-black; almost an adamantine lustre, sometimes somewhat greasy; S. white

Cerussite was first found when mining surface silver and copper ores, and magnificent specimens of crystallised cerussite occurred in the upper parts of the ore veins. Miners called them 'lead white' and, indeed, the name cerussite comes from the Latin *cerussa* ('white paint').

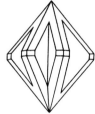

132 Cerussite — Příbram (Czech Republic); actual size of crystals up to 2 cm

Cerussite always originates as a product of the weathering of galena, especially in the parts of the ore veins which are easily accessible to surface water and carbon dioxide. Water frequently acts as a solvent to many minerals, and galena does not escape this process. Cerussite crystals have various forms, and they are often intertwinned in various regularly orientated arrangements. They have an exceptionally strong lustre. The rich druses of cerussite crystals from German deposits (particularly the Friedrichseegen mine near Ems, the Harz mountains and Johanngeorgenstadt in Saxony), and also those from the old deposit near the Czech town, Stříbro, adorn mineralogical collections all over the world. There are also abundant deposits at Nerchinsk in Russian Siberia and Colorado in the USA. Cerussite contains approximately 73 per cent lead, but it is important as a lead ore only in places where it occurs in extensive quantities. Strontianite (strontium carbonate) and witherite (barium carbonate) form crystals similar to the crystals of cerussite.

Azurite - *basic carbonate of copper*, $Cu(OHCO_3)_2$

Monoclinic; H. 3.5–4; Sp. gr. 3.7–3.9 g/cm³; blue; vitreous lustre; S. light blue

Azurite occurs in association with malachite from the weathering of any copper ores, and they are both responsible for the typical surface colouring of the ores. The crystals of azurite are of an exceptional, deeply blue colour and its granular, earthy or pulverulent covers are the colour of forget-me-nots. The richest deposits of azurite are at Tsumeb in Namibia, in the Cooper Queen Mine at Bisbee in Arizona, at Burraburra near Adelaide (South Australia) and Nizhni Tagil in the Urals (Russia). In Europe it is recovered at Chessy near Lyon (France), at Băita (Romania) and in Moldova.

Azurite is seldom used as an ornamental stone because it is too soft. However, when it is cut and polished it has a strong lustre and beautiful shades. Vividly colourful specimens of azurite with malachite are very popular among collectors. The vividness of the colours of specimens from some deposits (Banat in Romania, for instance) is further enhanced by the covers of yellow or rusty brown limonite. Azurite contains 55 per cent copper but is rarely extracted as an ore, because it hardly ever occurs in larger quantities. When ground, it can be used as a blue pigment and in the production of blue vitriol.

133 Azurite — Tsumeb (Namibia); actual size of crystals 10 cm

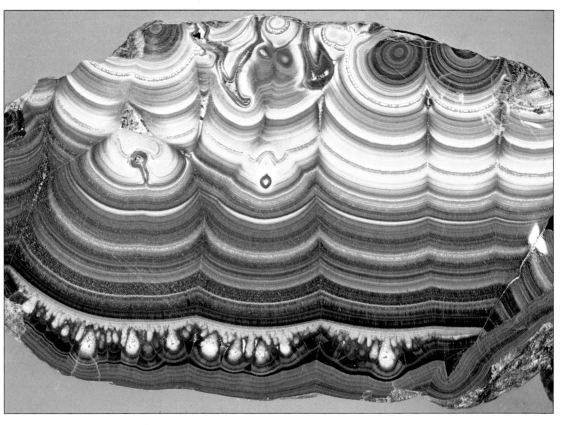

134   Malachite — Shaba (Zaire); actual size 13 x 7 cm

Malachite - *basic carbonate of copper*, $Cu_2(OH)_2CO_3$

Monoclinic; H. 4; Sp. gr. 4 g/cm³; green to dark green; vitreous, adamantine to silky lustre; S. green

Malachite is not just a modern ornamental stone. The Greeks and Romans used it to make amulets which, as they believed, were able to protect people, especially children, from various misfortunes. Malachite was also found by ancient miners in copper mines, where it occurred in the form of vivid green coatings, which at first were called 'rock green'; only later was it given its present name. However, malachite has also had other names, such as 'the velvet ore' or 'the satin ore'.

Malachite is the most common product of the weathering of copper and the ores of copper. It is abundantly present in the upper layers of all the deposits of copper ores. Apart from the surface covers, malachite commonly forms fine fibrous layers with a reniform surface or powdery efflorescences. In cavities it occurs exceptionally in the form of needle-shaped crystals. The best known deposits of the mineral are in extensive regions of the Urals, especially in the vicinity of Gumeshevsk, Bogoslovsk and Nizhni Tagil (Russia). The biggest malachite boulder, found at Gumeshevsk, weighed 60 tonnes. Other large deposits are in Zaire and at Tsumeb in Namibia, where it occurs with azurite. Azurite also accompanies malachite at other deposits, including Bisbee in Arizona (USA), Burraburra in Australia, Băita in Romania and Bertzdorf in Germany. The most recent deposit of malachite with an admixture of azurite is at Eilat in Israel; it is possible that this newly discovered deposit is a forgotten mine of the ancient Greeks and Romans. Malachite is both an ornamental stone and a valuable ore, containing approximately 57 per cent copper. The most beautiful specimens of worked malachite can be seen in the Winter Palace ('Hermitage') in St. Peterburg, Russia.

Chapter 6	SULPHATES AND SIMILAR COMPOUNDS	◁ 135 Barite — Dĕdova Hora (Czech Republic); actual size of crystals up to 2 cm

Sulphates are the salts of sulphuric acid. They are soft and of non-metallic appearance. They usually originate through deposition from sea water or through volcanic exhalations. Sometimes they result from the production of sulphuric acid during the oxidation of sulphides, mainly pyrite and marcasite.

Sulphates are divided into anhydrous (such as anhydrite and barite) and hydrous (such as gypsum and zippeite). Sulphates also include some groups of minerals of scientific and technical interest which, however, are not described in detail in this book. These are vitriols (hydrated sulphates of bivalent metals) – for example, melanterite (hydrated iron sulphate) or chalkantite (hydrated copper sulphate) – and alums (double hydrated sulphates of monovalent and trivalent metals or of bivalent and trivalent metals), for example, halotrichite (hydrated aluminium ferrous sulphate).

Related to sulphates are chromates (crocoite), tungstates (scheelite) and molybdates (wulfenite), which are primary minerals on ore deposits bound to granite magmata (scheelite) or secondary minerals of sulphidic deposits of hydrothermal origin.

Anhydrite - *calcium sulphate*, $CaSO_4$

Orthorhombic; H. 3.5; Sp. gr. 2.9–3.0 g/cm³; commonly white, colourless, bluish, grey, reddish; pearly lustre on cleavage surfaces, otherwise vitreous to greasy lustre; S. white

Anhydrite has a chemical composition similar to that of gypsum, for which it was originally mistaken. The name comes from the Greek *an* ('without') and *hydor* ('water'), for, in contrast to gypsum, anhydrite contains no water. It is usually compact and only exceptionally is it cleavable. Recoverable anhydrite deposits have been formed through deposition from sea water, just like the deposits of rock salt and gypsum.

136 Anhydrite — Staré Hory (Czech Republic); actual size of detail 3 x 3 cm

141

This is why anhydrite is often associated with gypsum, and sometimes alters to gypsum through absorption of water.

The most important deposits are at Wieliczka in Poland, where it forms layers of interesting shapes, the Salt Chamber in Austria, Berchtesgaden, Lüneburg and Stassfurt in Germany, Vulpino near Bergamo in Italy, Spišská Nová Ves in Slovakia, and the states of New Jersey and New York in the USA. Anhydrite remained unexploited for a long time and only recently has it become an important material for the chemical industry (production of sulphuric acid). Otherwise it has the same uses as gypsum.

Celestite - *strontium sulphate*, $SrSO_4$

Orthorhombic, H. 3–3.5; Sp. gr. 3.9–4.0 g/cm³; commonly blue, colourless, yellowish, reddish; vitreous to pearly lustre, somewhat greasy on fractured surface; S. white

Celestite, sometimes called celestine, has long been familiar to Bengali priests who used it to colour flames. With its help they prepared the vividly crimson Bengali lights, whose mysterious beauty filled believers with awe and horror. Not till much later did chemists discover that this flame colouring was caused by the element strontium, a component of celestite, while its relative, barium, colours the flame green-yellow. Chemists obtained volatile salts of both these metals from certain minerals, and mixed them with potassium chloride, charcoal and sulphur to make firework rockets.

The name celestite comes from the Latin *caelestis* ('heavenly'), after its sky-blue colour. Its crystals usually have the form of thick orthorhombic plates and columns. It is commonly found in sediments which developed from the skeletons of some radiolaria, in hydrothermal veins and cavities of igneous rocks. In Sicily and at Tarnobrzeg in Poland it occurs in crystal form. Industrially valuable deposits are near Bristol in the UK, at Mokatam in Egypt and at Lake Erie in the USA. Celestite is used in the chemical and food industries and for surgical and pyrotechnical purposes.

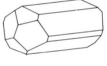

137 Celestite —
Špania Dolina
(Slovakia); actual
size of crystals 3 cm

Barite (barytes) - *barium sulphate*, BaSO₄

Orthorhombic, H. 3–3.5; Sp. gr. 4.48 g/cm³; white or variably coloured, usually greenish, yellowish, red, bluish, brown; vitreous lustre, pearly on some surfaces; S. white

Barite was familiar to the very first miners, for it occurs abundantly in ore veins. For a long time it was considered to be worthless gangue, though it stirred the interest of alchemists in the Middle Ages. Vincenzo Cascariolo, an Italian alchemist in Bologna, was heating barite with other minerals in the course of his experiments in 1630. He discovered that when heated it shines in the dark. This was the discovery of phosphorescence, which caused great excitement in those days. As Cascariolo studied the round clusters (nodules) of barite from gypsum marl in the vicinity of Bologna, the stone he discovered became known among his contemporary natural scientists as 'the shining ball of Bologna'.

Much later, when the nodules were examined in more detail, it was discovered that the 'shining balls' were the same mineral as the well-known heavy stone from the ore veins. Barite received its name from the Greek *barys* ('heavy'), because it was conspicuously and unusually heavy. The German name *Schwerspat* has a similar meaning. The high density of barite is close to the density of some of the iron ores, magnetite of haematite, for instance.

Barite occurs abundantly in cavities of ore veins in association with sulphide ores, especially lead, zinc and silver. It was formed by deposition from hot solutions rising from the interior of the Earth at higher temperatures. Often it forms separate veins or occurs in sedimentary deposits. The occurrence of separate barite veins, commonly containing an admixture of fluorite, happens usually in the closest association with granite massifs. The particular occurrence of compact barite found in such veins are the most important ores for practical use. The deposits in sedimentary rocks, where barite often forms nod-ules, are also valuable. It is also deposited from some hot springs.

Apart from its remarkable weight it is also distinctive in its often perfect crystals. They usually have the form of thick orthorhombic plates and columns, and are frequently very large. Some of the columnar crystallised varieties, which differ to a certain extent from the normally developed crystals, are classified as wolnyne. When pure, barite is colourless to white, but commonly it is tinted by various admixtures.

138   Barite — Dědova Hora (Czech Republic); actual size of crystal group16 x 8 cm

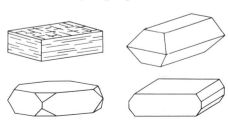

143

The chief world producers of barite are the USA, Germany (Meggen deposit in Westphalia) and the UK. Compact barite is of particular commercial value. However, from the mineralogical and collectors' point of view, barite crystals are much more interesting, particularly at many localities in the UK (mainly in Cumbria but also near Tavistock in Devon). From these noted deposits come large tabular crystals, pointed at each end, with the prevalent colours of greyish-yellow, blue-grey and honey yellow. These deposits are also known, apart from the plates, for their slender columnar crystals which are equally beautifully coloured. Other well known deposits are at Baia Sprie in Romania, Freiberg in Saxony, Příbram (Czech Republic) and Banská Štiavnica in Slovakia.

The present-day chemical industry makes the fullest use of barite especially in the manufacture of paints. Barite is added to the paints partly as a plain admixture and partly converted (by roasting) into barium sulphide; the white paint manufactured in this way is non-toxic and resistant to chemical attack. When ground, barite is used as a filling for paper and other substances, to give them weight. The ceramic industry uses barite in the manufacture of glazes and enamels. It is also used in the glass industry and in the production of barite cement and heavy concrete for protection against radioactive rays.

Barite as a raw material is also much sought after for the production of barium compounds needed in medicine (the barium meal given to patients before X-ray examination). The use of volatile barium salts for tinting flames (Bengali lights) for rockets and fireworks has already been mentioned.

139　Halotrichite — Dubník (Slovakia); actual size of detail 8 x 5.5 cm

Halotrichite - *hydrated aluminium ferrous sulphate*, $FeAl_2(SO_4)_4.22H_2O$

Monoclinic; H. 2.5; Sp. gr. 1.8–1.9 g/cm^2; colourless; silky lustre; S. white

Halotrichite was given the name from the Greek *als* ('salt') and *trichos* ('hair'). It is yet another water-soluble sulphate which often occurs during the decomposition of pyrite. Halotrichite is one of the most common natural alums. It is often associated with its relative pickeringite, hydrated magnesium aluminium sulphate. Halotrichite crystallises in capillary, fibrous, acicular crystals, which usually occur as efflorescence on slates. The main deposits are Mörsfeld in Rhineland (Germany), Červenica-Dubník in Slovakia, along the Gila river in New Mexico (USA), at Copiapó in Chile and Urmiah in Iran. Halotrichite is not as yet used commercially.

Another interesting mineral of the alum group is tschermigite (the term derives from the name of the deposit at Čermníky near Kadaň, Czech Republic. Tschermigite is hydrous aluminium ammonium sulphate. It forms layers in clay and coal pit heaps, generally with numerous other sulphates; the tabular layers are composed of fibres which are orientated perpendicularly towards the plane of the layers. The crystallised form is rare.

Gypsum - *hydrated calcium sulphate*, $CaSO_4.2H_2O$

Monoclinic; H. 1.5–2; Sp. gr. 2.3–2.4 g/cm^3; commonly colourless, white, yellowish, red to blood-red, grey to black; vitreous lustre, pearly on cleavage surfaces, silky lustre in the fibrous variety; S. white

140 Gypsum (selenite) — Ekaterinburg, the Urals (Russia); actual size 8 x 5.5 cm

141   Gypsum — Biskra (Algeria); actual size of crystals 3 cm

Gypsum has been known since antiquity. The 4th century BC Greek sculptor Lysippus of Sicyon was the first to use plaster manufactured from gypsum. According to Pliny the Elder, he made the very first plaster cast of a human face.

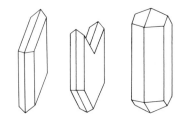

Gypsum was probably the first mineral to be studied under the microscope in 1695 by Anton van Leeuwenhoek, a Dutch natural scientist, originally a merchant in Delft and the founder of microscopy.

Gypsum forms tabular or columnar crystals. The tabular crystals resemble mica ('Maria glass'). When pure, crystalline gypsum is clear and massive gypsum is white. Most frequently, however, it is tainted yellow or brown, according to the admixtures present. When finely granular it is called alabaster; when it is fibrous, it is called selenite. The name alabaster was derived from the Greek *alabastros* and is said to originate from the name of the Egyptian town Alabastron. The name selenite is also as old as the mineral classification system itself. Intergrown gypsum crystals often form 'swallow tails'; they also become rounded to a lenticular shape or gather to form star-shaped agglomerates. Gypsum can be scratched with a fingernail, by which it is distinguishable from similar minerals.

Exploitable deposits of gypsum developed by deposition from sea water, often in association with anhydrite, which often alters into gypsum through water absorption. Deposits interesting to the mineralogist originate also through the weathering of pyrites, for example in ore veins and in coal seams.

The most noted gypsum deposits are near Volterra (Tuscany), in Spain and Egypt, where it occurs abundantly and is recovered. Other large deposits are in a number of localities in the USA, in France, UK, Austria (the Salt Chamber), Poland (near Wieliczka) and a number of other places. At many sites in the Sahara, perfectly developed agglomerates of gypsum crystals occur, lying loosely in sand. This gypsum sometimes contains more than 50 per cent fine grains of sand which it drew into its brownish, greyish or yellowish lenticular crystals during a rapid process of crystallisation. These interesting formations are commonly flat, quite often fairly large and grouped into shapes resembling roses in bloom, or other flowers and leaves. This is why they are called 'desert roses'. Such formations originated through evaporation of water from salt lakes or through the decomposition of pyrite.

Gypsum is used mainly for the production of plaster. When heated to 300–400°C it yields plaster of Paris, which sets hard after being mixed with water. When gypsum is exposed to a temperature above 400°C it does not absorb water. It is then used in paints and cement. Alabaster is suitable for sculpture; selenite, highly popular for its unusual lustre, is a precious stone. Less frequently gypsum is used for the production of sulphuric acid and sulphur.

Zippeite - *complex hydrated sulphate of uranium*, $U_2SO_{10}+3-6H_2O$

Monoclinic; H. 3; Sp. gr. 2.5 g/cm³; grey-yellow to lemon white; S. white

Zippeite's striking appearance caught the attention of a Czech metallurgist, Adolf Patera, in the 1850s, when the fame of the Jáchymov silver mines was in decline. On top of the large, forgotten pit heaps, powdery minerals began to appear, vividly coloured, originating from the decomposition of pitchblende. These colourful layers, in which zippeite prevailed, gave Patera the idea of utilising the uranium minerals in the manufacture of paints. Mining began in 1859 not only for the products which resulted

142   Zippeite — Shinkolobwe, Shaba (Zaire); actual size of detail 9 x 6 cm

143   Crocoite — Dundas, Tasmania (Australia); actual size 7.5 x 7.5 cm

from uraninite decomposition but for uraninite itself. A variety of yellow paints were manufactured because among all the secondary minerals on the pit heap there was a prevalence of the yellow powdery coatings.

Zippeite is one of the so-called 'uranium ochres'. It occurs in association with uranopilite, a monoclinic, very complex hydrated alkaline sulphate of uranium, from which it hardly differs in appearance, and with other secondary uranium minerals in the weathered veins of uranium. Zippeite was named after the Prague mineralogist, F.X.M. Zippe (1791–1863). Apart from Jáchymov in the Czech Republic, the mineral occurs mainly near Wölsendorf in Bavaria (Germany) and at Fruita in Utah (USA). Zippeite is no longer used for the manufacture of paints. It serves as a source of radioactive elements, as does pitchblende.

Crocoite - *lead chromate*, PbCrO$_4$

Monoclinic; H. 2.5–3; Sp. gr. 5.9–6 g/cm^3; orange yellow; greasy to adamantine lustre; S. orange

Crocoite is a comparatively rare mineral, but the first one in which the element chromium was discovered. This success was earned by the French chemist Louis Vauquelin in 1797, when he experimented with crocoite from the Urals. Crocoite forms beautiful, fiery coloured crystals, columnar to needle-shaped. It occurs in chromite deposits, in quartz veins and in the oxidation zones of lead lodes.

The most important deposits are at Berezovsky in the Urals (Russia) and at Dundas in Tasmania (Australia). Crocoite occurs less abundantly at Băita in Romania, at Labo on Luzon island (Philippines), at Congonhas da Campo and Gaya Beyra in Brazil and in the Penchalonga mine in Zimbabwe. Beautiful specimens were recovered from the newly discovered deposit at Chemnitz in Saxony. As it is very uncommon, crocoite is not important as an ore of chromium although this metal was first discovered in it.

144   Scheelite — Fürstenberg (Germany); actual size of crystal 1.5 cm

Scheelite - *calcium tungstate*, CaWO$_4$

Tetragonal; H. 4.5–5; Sp. gr. 5.9–6.1 g/cm³; commonly grey-white, yellowish, brownish, brown to reddish, less commonly yellow to greenish, very rarely colourless; greasy, often even adamantine lustre; S. white

Scheelite was often found in cassiterite mines in the Czech Erzgebirge (Ore Mountains) and miners called it 'the white bronze hailstone' (in contrast to the so-called 'black hailstone' of cassiterite). Axel Cronstedt, a Swedish metallurgist and chemist, gave

a more accurate description of this mineral in the mid-18th century. He considered the mineral to be an iron ore and named it 'tungsten' (heavy stone). A detailed description and a first chemical analysis of the mineral came from his countryman, K.W. Scheele, in 1781, who discovered the element tungsten in it. The mineral was later named scheelite in his honour by the French mineralogist, F. Beaudant (1781–1850).

Scheelite crystallises in bipyramids, often rounded. It occurs fairly abundantly in cassiterite and tungstate deposits. It crystallises from hot solutions, frequently under the influence of gases (pneumatolytically) and occurs in quartz veins in granites and gneisses. Crystallised specimens of scheelite are greatly valued and are a gem of any collection.

Scheelite is found at Zinnwald (Germany) and Cínovec (Czech Republic), where it forms tiny, pale brown crystals and druses in quartz, together with zinnwaldite. Other deposits are at Schwarzenberg in Saxony, Cornwall in England and in Connecticut (USA). It is recovered as an important ore of tungsten.

The mineral stolzite is also included in this group; it was named after J. A. Stolz, a doctor from Teplice (Czech Republic) who was the first to describe it as a separate mineral. It is lead wolframate (PbWO$_4$), which forms tiny tetragonal rounded crystals resembling (in shape) scheelite. The crystals are often grouped in sheaf-shaped and globose clusters. Small quantities of stolzite occur in quartz at Cínovec in northern part of the Czech Republic, where it was first described.

Wulfenite - *lead molybdate*, PbMoO$_4$

Tetragonal; H. 3; Sp. gr. 6.7–6.9 g/cm³; commonly orange yellow, orange, yellow-grey to brownish; adamantine to greasy lustre; S. white or light grey

145 Wulfenite — Mežica (Slovenia); actual size of crystals up to 3 cm

146 Wulfenite — Los Lamentos (Mexico); actual size 11 cm

147   Wulfenite — Los Lamentos (Mexico); actual size of detail 6.5 x 6 cm

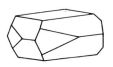
Wulfenite, named after the Austrian mineralogist A. Wulfen, who was the first to describe it in 1785, is a rare and beautiful mineral. It crystallises in bipyramids, plates to leaflets, and occasionally in short columns. It occurs through the oxidation of galena and therefore is mainly found in the oxidation zones of lead ores.

The main deposits are at Bleiberg in Carinthia (Austria), in Höllenthal near Garmisch (Germany), Mežica in Slovenia, Băita in Romania, Phoenixville in Pennsylvania (USA) and in Australia. Specimens of exceptional beauty, consisting of rich clusters of orange to brown, thick tabular crystals with irregular edges, are found in large quantities near Villa Ahumada in the Sierra de los Lamentos mountain range in the Chihuahua province in Mexico. Crystals embedded in parent rock have a very small number of faces and their average size is 2–4 cm. Where wulfenite occurs in sufficient quantities it is recovered as a lead ore. Pure wulfenite contains up to 55 per cent lead.

Chapter 7

PHOSPHATES AND SIMILAR COMPOUNDS

This group, which contains not only phosphates and salts of phosphoric acid, but also arsenates and the rare vanadates, is the second largest group, next to silicates. Phosphates usually occur in pegmatites and as a product of the weathering of other minerals. Almost all arsenates and vanadates develop secondarily on ore deposits. In this group, too, we distinguish between the anhydrous salts (for example, apatite, pyromorphite), the hydrous salts (for example, vivianite, variscite), and the alkaline salts (lazulite and others). The minerals in the phosphate group usually display isomorphism, where not only metals but also phosphorus, arsenic and vanadium may substitute for, or mix with, each other. In many alkaline salts the hydroxyl is often substituted by halogen elements (as for instance in amblygonite). An interesting and distinct isomorphous group is represented by uranium mica, so-called because of its crystal shape and perfect cleavage. A large isomorphous group is composed of minerals — apatite, pyromorphite, mimetesite and others — which mix together. Only rarely does one come across a mineral which is a phosphate or a similar compound and which does not mix with other minerals (such as lazulite).

149 Lazulite — Stickelberg (Austria); actual size of detail 12 x 9 cm

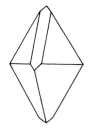

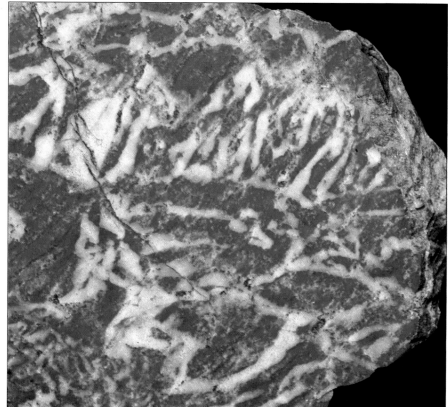

◁
148 Apatite — Wilberforce (Canada); actual size of crystals 2 cm

Lazulite - *basic aluminium-magnesium phosphate with iron*, $(Mg,Fe)Al_2(OHPO_4)_2$

Monoclinic-pseudorhombic; H. 5–6; Sp. gr. 3.0 g/cm³; blue; vitreous lustre; S. colourless

The name lazulite is derived from the Arab *lazul* ('sky') and Greek *lithos* ('stone'). It has always been known as a decorative stone, but was never highly valued; it was mainly used as an imitation of more precious stones. The Arabs passed it for turquoise or the more valuable lazurite (lapis lazuli). This is why it is sometines called 'imitation lapis'.

Lazulite occurs in pegmatites, in quartz veins and in metamorphic rocks rich in aluminium. It is usually granular to compact, and only rarely forms sharp needle-shaped or tabular crystals. The crystals seemingly have orthorhombic symmetry and commonly are twinned according to two different laws.

The most famous European deposit is at Werfen, near Salzburg (Austria). Interesting specimens are also found in smaller European deposits, particularly at Krieglach in Styria (Austria), where massive lazulite is found, at Zermatt (Switzerland) and Horjösberg in Wermland (Sweden). Outside Europe the largest deposits are in the USA and Brazil: at Crowder's Mountain in North Carolina lazulite is found fairly abundantly in flexible micaceous quartzites. The Graves Mountain deposits in Georgia are noted for the best crystal specimens. The dark blue crystals from Tijuco in Minas Gerais state, Brazil, are the ones most suitable as gemstones. Today lazulite is most frequently ground to lenticular shape or used for the manufacture of small ornamental objects.

Pseudomalachite - *basic phosphate of copper*, $Cu_5(OHPO_4)_2$

Monoclinic; H. 4–4.5; Sp. gr. 4.35 g/cm³; pistachio green to blackish green; greasy lustre; S. green

Pseudomalachite was given its name because of its close resemblance to malachite. However, it also has other local names, for example, lunnite in honour of the chemist Lunn, or ehlite because of the discovery of its deposits at Ehle in the Rhineland (Germany). It is also known as phosphorochalcite. Not until fairly recently was it confirmed that all these minerals are identical.

Pseudomalachite forms rich emerald green reniform aggregates with a ra-

150 Pseudomalachite — L'ubietová (Slovakia); actual size of aggregates up to 3 cm

dial structure, or thin shapeless coatings. It develops as a secondary mineral in copper ores, especially chalcopyrite. Usually it is found in association with malachite. The main deposits are in Rhineland and Siberia, in the surroundings of Chotěboř (Czech Republic) and at Lubietová in Slovakia. Pseudomalachite has no practical use because it never occurs in substantial quantities. It is extracted only as a component admixed to copper ores.

Brazilianite - *basic aluminium-sodium phosphate*, $NaAl_3[(OH)_2PO_4]_2$

Monoclinic; H. 5.5; Sp. gr. 2.98 g/cm³; yellow to green-yellow; vitreous lustre; S. white

Brazilianite is one of the newly discovered minerals. It was identified by the American mineralogists Pough and Henderson in 1945 and named after the country in which it had been discovered. Brazilianite occurs in the form of perfect crystals grouped in druses, in pegmatites, and is often of precious-stone quality. It was first found near the town Conselheira in Minas Gerais state, Brazil. During the past few years this deposit has yielded a great quantity of raw material which has included crystals of surprisingly large dimensions and perfectly bounded crystal faces. Some of these are found on leaves of muscovite, with their strong silvery glitter, ingrown in the parent rock. Such fine specimens are not ground but are kept in museums and private collections. The most exquisite crystals, dark greenish-yellow to olive green in colour, are sometimes as long as 12 cm and up to 8 cm wide. In recent years, crystals of a similar shape and dimension have been discovered in another deposit in Minas Gerais, near Mantena, but they lack the perfection of the crystal bounding. Recently, brazilianites have been found in

151   Brazilianite — Minas Gerais (Brazil); actual size of crystals 5.5 x 4.5 and 6 x 3.5 cm

the Palermo and Charles Davis mines near North Croton (Grafton county) in New Hampshire (USA), and these are sought after by collectors.

The rare vésigniéite, a monoclinic basic vanadate of copper and barium, $BaCu_3(OHVO_4)_2$, is related to brazilianite. It forms tabular and powdery aggregates of green to yellow-green colour. It occurs in the oxidation zone of ore veins, for example at Horní Kalná in north-eastern region of the Czech Republic and at Vrančice near Příbram in central Bohemia.

Apatite - *phosphate of calcium with fluorine and chlorine*, $Ca_5(F, ClOH)(PO_4)_3$

Hexagonal; H. 5; Sp. gr. 3.16–3.22 g/cm³; commonly blue-green, green grey, white, brown; greasy lustre; S. white

Apatite got its name from the Greek *apaté* ('deceit'). Ancient mineralogists mistakenly believed that every mineral had its own characteristic colour. They took apatite for many varied minerals, such as aquamarine, amethyst or tourmaline. When, at the end of the 18th century, its chemical composition was determined and apatite was established as a separate mineral, it was aptly named apatite, for its misleading appearance, by Abraham Gottlob Werner, professor at the Mining Academy in Freiberg.

Apatite occurs in a variety of colours and also in a variety of forms. Its crystals may be thick tabular, columnar or elongated to needle-shaped. It also occurs in massive, granular radial and compact forms. The compact or radial crystals are called phosphorite. Phosphorites are not completely chemically pure apatites because of the presence of various impurities and organic remains. Their colour usually ranges within a wide variety of different shades of grey. Their origin is explained by several theories, and some of them contradict each other. In general, organisms take compounds of

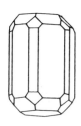

152 Apatite — Greifenstein, Saxony (Germany); actual size of crystals up to 1.5 cm

153   Apatite — Durango (Mexico); actual size of crystals 1.5 cm

154   Staffelite — Staffel, Lower Saxony (Germany); actual size of detail 11 x 8 cm

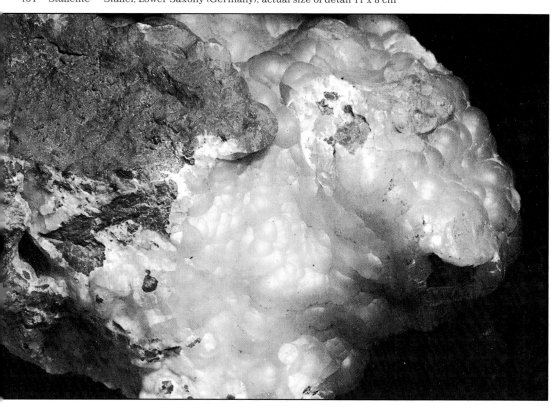

phosphorus from sea water and accumulate them in the hard parts of their bodies. When they die, the phosphate gradually released (leached) from their bodies is deposited often in colloidal form, particularly in poorly aerated waters.

Apatites are found in most rocks, especially in pegmatites and in cassiterite deposits, but not in large quantities. Phosphorites, whose basic component is apatite, often form whole series of rock strata. Staffelite is a stalactitic apatite and occurs in the Staffel deposits near Limburg, Germany.

The largest deposits of phosphates used for commercial purposes are in the USA (Florida and Tennessee), yielding almost half of the world's production of phosphates. Further deposits are in northern Africa (Morocco, Tunisia, Algeria and Egypt), in Kazakhstan, the Ukraine and the Kola peninsula in the north of Russia. The best known apatite crystals come from St. Gotthard (Switzerland), Saxony (Germany), Quebec (Canada) and Durango (Mexico).

Phosphates are used in the manufacture of fertilisers. The attractively coloured apatite varieties are used as ornamental stones. The brilliant cuts of the pink and yellow Swiss apatites are well known, and quite beautiful. The yellow-green apatites, which are also very popular as semiprecious stones, are traditionally called 'asparagus stones' because of their colour.

Pyromorphite - *phosphate of lead with chlorine*, $Pb_5Cl(Po_4)_3$

Hexagonal; H. 3.5–4; Sp. gr. 6.7–7.0 g/cm³; commonly green or brown, rarely yellow, orange, white to colourless; adamantine to greasy lustre; S. whitish

Pyromorphite has been known for a long time, though it has been called several names, according to its colour. The present name originated from the Greek words *pyr* ('fire') and *morph* ('form'), for it used to be thought that the crystals were a product of volcanic magma. Today it is known that, on the contrary, it is formed in the upper zone of lead veins in association with cerussite and a number of other secondary minerals, which originated through the decompostion of galena. It is by far the most conspicuous of all these minerals owing to its glaring 'poisonous-looking' colour and to the shape of its crystals. The crystals are usually columnar, often perfectly bounded by smooth

155 Pyromorphite — Bad Ems (Germany); actual size of crystals 22 mm

faces and grouped in rich druses. On rare occasions the mineral forms reniform or radial aggregates.

The conspicuously green colouring influenced its earlier German name, *Grünbleierz*, whereas when pyromorphite was found in the less common brown variety it was called *Braunbleierz*. Pyromorphite with an admixture of calcium is miesite, given this name according to the locality in Bohemia where it occurred (Mies in German; the Czech name is Stříbro). The miesite found at Stříbro had the form of whitish radial aggregates and occurred in association with brown pyromorphite.

The main deposits of pyromorphite are at Clausthal in the Harz mountains and Johanngorgenstadt in Saxony (Germany), Cornwall in England, Příbram in the Czech Republic, Banská Štiavnica in Slovakia, Berezovsk in the Urals and Nerchinsk in the Transbaikal region (Russia), Phoenixville in Pennsylvania (USA), and Mindouli in Congo. Where pyromorphite is found in association with other lead ores in larger quantities, it also serves as a lead ore, containing 75 per cent lead.

Vanadinite - *lead vanadate with chlorine*, $Pb_5Cl(VO_4)_3$

Hexagonal; H. 3; Sp. gr. 6.8–7.1 g/cm³; commonly brownish, yellow to ruby red; nearly adamantine or strong vitreous lustre; S. white

Vanadinite forms columnar, rarely pyramidal crystals, or fibrous aggregates with reniform surface; it also occurs massive. Vanadinite develops in the oxidation zone of lead ores. The main deposits are at Obir mountain in Carinthia (Austria), Berezovsk in the Urals, Sierra de Córdoba in Argentina, Zimapan in Mexico, Arizona (USA), Algeria, Morocco, and Australia.

Vanadinite was once an important ore of vanadium (it contains 19.4 per cent vanadium pentoxide). The alloy of vanadium and iron (ferro-vanadium) is used for the manufacture of special steels. Vanadium pentoxide is an important catalyst in the manufacture of sulphuric acid. Today, however, vanadium is gained mainly as a by-product of the processing of some iron ores (Taberg in Sweden, the Urals) and is also recovered from bauxite-processing sediments.

156 Vanadinite — Mibladen (Morocco); actual size of the largest crystal 8 mm

157 Vanadinite — Djebel Mahser (Morocco); actual size of crystals 2–2.5 mm

158 Mimetite — Tsumeb (Namibia); actual size of aggregates up to 1 cm

159 Campylite — Příbram (Czech Republic); actual size of aggregates 4–9 mm

Campylite - *arsenate and phosphate of lead with chlorine*, $Pb_5Cl[(As,P)O_4]_3$

Hexagonal; H. 3.5–4; Sp. gr. 6.7–7.1 g/cm³; yellow to orange; adamantine to greasy lustre; S. whitish

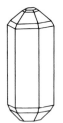

Campylite takes its name from the Greek *kampylos* ('bent'), on account of the barrel-shaped bend of its crystals. It is composed of pyromorphite and mimetite (lead arsenate with chlorine), and usually occurs in association with them. It occurs in the upper parts of lead ore deposits through the oxidation of galena or cerussite. Its main deposits are at Příbram (Czech Republic) and Roghton Gill in Cumbria (England). Campylite is a comparatively rare mineral.

Another rare mineral is mimetesite, or mimetite, whose name is derived from the Greek *mimetes* ('imitator'), for it resembles in shape the crystals of pyromorphite, for which it used to be mistaken. Most commonly it forms hexagonal yellowish columns, usually in rounded barrel-shaped forms, which are typical of campylite; in this it differs from pyromorphite. The chief sources are at Johanngeorgenstadt in Saxony (Germany), Nerchinsk in eastern Siberia (Russia), Tsumeb in Namibia, in Chihuahua (Mexico) and in Phoenixville in Pennsylvania (USA).

Variscite - *hydrated aluminium phosphate*, $AlPO_4.2H_2O$

Orthorhombic-pseudohexagonal; H. 4–5; Sp. gr. 2.52 g/cm³; bluish-green, white to colourless; waxy lustre; S. colourless

Variscite is a very attractive but little known precious stone, which is often mistaken for other minerals. Variscite was described in 1837 by Friedrich Adolf Breithaupt, a German mineralogist from Vogtland in southern Thuringia. Variscite was named after the old name of this region, Variscia. Crystals of the same mineral were found in 1894 on the western shore of Lake Utah in the USA, and were named utahlite. Later it was found that they were the same mineral. Now the name utahlite is applied mainly to the semiprecious varieties of variscite. A variety rich in iron is called redontite.

Variscite occurs in the form of radially fibrous aggregates and crusts with reniform surfaces, and occasionally in indistinct columnar crystals. It fills cracks and cavities of rocks rich in aluminium, mainly in silicate schists and greywackes, often in association with amorphous aluminium phosphates.

The loveliest specimens of variscite are egg-shaped to spherical tubers, which are found in breccia cavities of sedimentary rocks in the Clay Canyon near Fairfield, Utah. Most of these concretions do not, however, exceed the average size of 7–10 cm (though several specimens up to 30 cm long have been recovered), and many are suitable only to be polished into a plate; only some can be used as gemstones, ground and polished to a lenticular shape. Variscite, both on its own and in association with other phosphates, especially wardite (hydrated basic phosphate of aluminium and sodium) is an extremely attractive stone.

160   Variscite — Lewiston, Utah (USA); actual size 10 x 7 cm

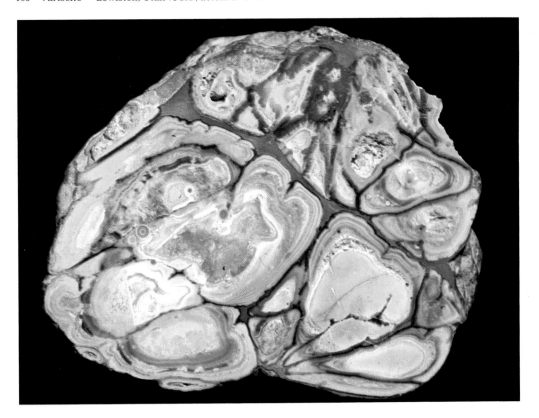

Wavellite - *hydrous basic phosphate of aluminium*, $Al_3(OH)_3(PO_4)_2.5H_2O$

Orthorhombic; H. 3.5–4; Sp. gr. 2.3–2.4g /cm³; colourless, whitish to yellow-green, occasionally green, blue to brown; vitreous lustre; S. white

Wavellite was first discovered in 1800 at Barnstaple in Devon (UK) and was described by the English physicist, W. Wavell. Larger quantities of this mineral were discovered at the beginninig of the 19th century near Třenice (Czech Republic), when mining iron ores and quarrying for building stone. Wavellite usually forms radial bunches, which are mostly round; sometimes it may also form small needle-shaped crystals. It occurs in sedimentary rocks, such as greywackes and sandstones, where it developed by alteration and crystallisation from the dissolved shells of various animals. The best known deposits, apart from the Czech Republic and Devon are at Langenstriegis near Freiberg in Saxony (Germany), the world-famous magnetite mines near Kirunavaara in northern Sweden, at Chester in Pennsylvania (USA) and at Ouro Preto in Brazil. Wavellite has hardly any industrial significance. In some places in the USA, however, it occurs in substantial quantities and is recovered as a raw material for obtaining phosphorus, which was previously mainly used for the manufacture of matches. Today paints are still made from it at Harrisburg (Pennsylvania). Though wavelite is a fairly common mineral, it is much sought after by collectors on account of its conspicuous radial bunches. Lumps with wavelite in globular form and with the relatively abundant zepharowichite (microscopically compact wavellite) are particularly popular, mainly those from deposits in the Czech Republic.

161   Wavellite — Cerhovice (Czech Republic); actual size of aggregates up to 2 cm

162 Vivianite — Ashio (Japan); actual size of crystals up to 2 cm

Vivianite - *hydrated iron phosphate* $Fe_3(PO_4)_2.8H_2O$

Monoclinic; H. 2; Sp. gr. 2.6–2.7 g/cm³; light to dark blue to greenish; vitreous lustre, pearly on some faces, with partial metallic shades; S. colourless to blue-white, quickly turning to indigo blue

Vivianite was discovered at the beginning of the 18th century by the British mineralogist J. G. Vivian in pyrrhotite veins near St. Agnes in Cornwall, UK. Abraham Gottlob Werner named the mineral in Vivian's honour in 1817. Later the mineral was discovered in substantial quantities in other deposits, first in massive form, later also as crystals. Vivianite crystals are commonly columnar or tabular, often in star-shaped or round groups. It is also earthy or powdery (in peat bogs). When fresh it is clear, but when exposed to oxygen it turns immediately blue or green. This happens because the bivalent iron in the vivianite partially changes into trivalent iron. Vivianite develops in pyrite deposits, mostly through the weathering of the pyrites, through decomposition of organic residues in peat-bogs and in bog-iron ores, and also in coprolites (fossil faeces), where it usually forms star-shaped aggregates, together with gypsum. The chief deposits include Bodenmais in Bavaria (Germany), Cornwall (UK), Czech Republic, Kerch in the Crimea (Ukraine), Cameroon, and Mullica Hills in New Jersey (USA). Vivianite is of no commercial value so far, but the large and well developed crystals, especially those found in Cameroon, are popular with collectors.

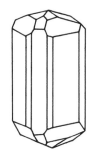

Turquoise - *hydrated basic phosphate of aluminium and copper,*

$$CuAl_6[(OH)_2PO_4]_4.4H_2O$$

Triclinic; H. 5–6; Sp. gr. 2.6–2.8 g/cm³; commonly green-blue, blue to grey-green; faint waxy lustre; S. white

163 Turquoise — Anatolia (Turkei); actual size 4 x 3 cm

Turquoise was a most popular precious stone, especially during the period of the Ottoman Empire. The Turks bought the stone and transported it to Persia. They also had old turquoise mines in the Sinai peninsula which was then part of the Ottoman Empire. However, these mines, which had been worked even in the days of ancient Egypt, were in the hands of wild, hostile tribes, and the Turks had to pay dearly for the Sinai turquoise. There were, at that time, also small deposits in Anatolia (Turkey). Turquoise is a cryptocrystalline mineral. It is commonly reniform or stalactitic, or may form a coating. It occurs as a filling in cracks in extrusive rocks and sandstones, occasionally in pegmatites. The main deposits are: Mashhad and Ma'dan, near Neyshabur, in Iran, Karatybe near Samarkand in Uzbekistan, Mont Chalchitl near Los Cerillos in New Mexico, Utah and California in the USA. In Europe turquoise occurs in Jordanów in Upper Silesia (Poland). The attractively coloured varieties are used as precious stones.

164 Wardite — Livingstone, Utah (USA); actual size 6 cm

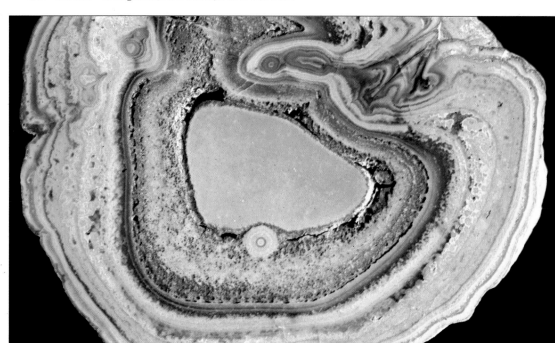

Wardite - *complex hydrated basic phosphate of aluminium and sodium,*

$$Na_4Al_{12}(OH)_{16}(PO_4)_8.8H_2O$$

Tetragonal; H. 5; Sp. gr. 2.8 g/cm³; pale green to blue-green; waxy lustre; S. colourless

Wardite is one of the least known precious stones. It was first described by the American mineralogist Davis after it was found in Cedar Valley near Lake Utah (USA), so far the only place where it has been found. It appears there in small quantities in association with variscite (utahlite), on whose nodules it forms oolitic to compact coatings. As a precious stone it comes into consideration only when together with variscite.

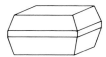

165   Torbernite — Horní Slavkov (Czech Republic); actual size of crystals 8 mm

Torbernite - *hydrated phosphate of uranium and copper,* $Cu(UO_2PO_4)_2.8\text{-}12H_2O$

Tetragonal; H. 2–2.5; Sp. gr. 3.3 g/cm³; emerald green; pearly lustre; S. apple green

Autunite – *hydrated phosphate of uranium and calcium,* $Ca(UO_2PO_4)_2.8\text{-}12H_2O$

Tetragonal; H. 2–2.5; Sp. gr. 3.2 g/cm³; yellow to yellow-green, sulphur yellow; intense vitreous lustre, often pearly on some faces; S. yellow

Torbernite and autunite belong among the uranium micas. Miners on both sides of the Erzgebirge (Ore Mountains) in Saxony and Bohemia found torbernite and autunite in the ore veins long ago. They called them 'green mica'. The first scientific reference to the mineral was made at the end of the 18th century by Ignatius Born (1742–1791), professor of Prague University, and by Abraham Gottlob Werner (1749–1817), a mineralogist and geologist from Freiberg.

The uranium micas most commonly crystallise in thin tabular plates, often well bounded, with excellent 'mica-type' cleavage. They occur more abundantly as leaf-like aggregates or bunches on the walls of cracks, originating from the weathering of uraninite. The main deposits are in Cornwall (England), the Tannenbaum gallery in Johanngeorgenstadt in Saxony (Germany), Jáchymov (Czech Republic), Brancheville in Connecticut (USA), Tchinkolobwe and Kasolo in Zaire, and Watsonville in Australia. Uranium micas are important raw materials for the production of uranium and its compounds. Autunite contains 60 per cent of the U_3O_8 oxide, torbernite 55–60 per cent.

166   Natrolite — Zálezly (Czech Republic);
actual size of crystals 1 cm

167   Cut olivine — Zebirget (Egypt); actual
size 30.8 x 18.8 mm, weight 66.43 carat

Chapter 8

SILICATES

This is the largest and commonest group of minerals, for it represents approximately 40 per cent of all minerals. In some silicates, aluminium replaces silicon. Such minerals are then called aluminosilicates (feldspar, kaolinite, for instance). Detailed system-atization of silicates is rather complicated and is determined by the arrangement of the internal constituent units of each mineral. Some silicates which resemble each other in their chemical structure often intermingle, thus forming natural groups. The minerals of such groups (such as garnets, pyroxenes, feldspars) share similar characteristics. Zeolites form a special group of silicates — crystalline hydrated aluminosilicates of light metals. The trait in which they differ from other hydrated crystalline minerals is that their water can be removed without disturbing their internal structure and crystal form. Silicates occur in the mineral world in a variety of ways, as primary or secondary minerals in igneous or metamorphic rocks.

Olivine - *silicate of magnesium and iron,* $(Mg,Fe)_2SiO_4$

Orthorhombic; H. 6.5–7; Sp. gr. 3.5 g/cm³, on average; commonly yellow-green to olive green; vitreous lustre, somewhat greasy when fractured; S. white

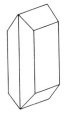
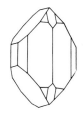

Olivine was sought after as a precious stone in ancient Rome, and it was originally found in a small island which the Romans called Topazos. According to the name of the island the stone was given the name *topazus*, which is frequently mentioned in Latin works. Subsequent commentaries on these sources gave the impression, quite wrongly, that the Roman topazus was the stone now known as topaz. The large ancient deposit was eventually forgotten, and it was thought that the Roman topazus came from the Orient, perhaps from India.

Later, deposits of this stone were found in Europe. Anselmus Boëtius de Boot wrote that olivine was recovered on the hill of Kozákov (Czech Republic). The mineral was called chrysolite, from Greek *chrysos* ('gold') and *lithos* ('stone').

Kozákov remained the sole known deposit of this precious stone until 1900, but then olivine was discovered in the Egyptian islands of Zebirget (St. John's) in the Red Sea and it eventually emerged that the main island of this group was the 'lost' island of Topazos. The rich deposit soon regained its fame and today, once again, it represents the main source in the world, for Egyptian olivines are extremely pure and, more important, of considerable size.

Olivine occurs most commonly in the form of grains, usually grouped into granular agglomerates. The loose grains of olivine often resemble tiny chippings of green glass. Crystals, which most often are columnar, are rare. Olivine turns yellow or red when exposed to oxygen. Mostly it occurs in substantial quantities in the upper layers of igneous rocks with a small part of silicon dioxide, especially in basalt. Sometimes olivines form independent rocks called peridotites.

The main deposits include St. John's, Arizona, Brazil, New Zealand, and, in Europe, Norway, the vicinity of Kozákov hill (Czech Republic) and Forstberg near Mayen in the Eifel mountains (Germany). The transparent olivine varieties, which are also called chrysolite or peridot (an old French name of unknown origin) are still used as precious stones.

Much rarer than olivine are minerals of similar composition, including hortonolite, silicate of magnesium and iron $(Fe,Mg)_2SiO_4$; forsterite, magnesium silicate Mg_2SiO_4; and fayalite, iron silicate Fe_2SiO_4.

168   Olivine — Podmoklice (Czech Republic); actual size 5 cm

169   Pyrope — central Bohemian highlands (Czech Republic); diameter of bore core 11 cm

Garnets - *binary silicates of bivalent and trivalent elements*

Cubic; vitreous to greasy lustre; S. white

Pyrope - *magnesium-aluminium sillicate*, $Mg_3Al_2(SiO_4)_3$
H. 7–7.5; Sp. gr. 3.7–3.8 g/cm³; commonly red

Almandine - *iron-aluminium silicate*, $Fe_3Al_2(SiO_4)_3$
H. 7; Sp. gr. 4.1–4.3 g/cm³; commonly red

Andradite - *calcium-iron silicate*, $Ca_3Fe_2(SiO_4)_3$
H. 6.6–7.5; Sp. gr. 3.7–4.1 g/cm³; commonly greenish

Grossular - *calcium-aluminium silicate*, $Ca_3Al_2(SiO_4)_3$
H. 6.5–7.5; Sp. gr. 3.7–4.3 g/cm³; commonly green or red-brown (hessonite)

Spessartite - *manganese-aluminium silicate*, $Mn_3Al_2(SiO_4)_3$
H. 7; Sp. gr. 3.77–4.27 g/cm³; commonly reddish

Uvarovite - *calcium-chromium silicate*, $Ca_3Cr_2(SiO_4)_3$
H. 6.5–7.5; Sp. gr. 3.42 g/cm³; emerald green with yellow-green shades

Garnets were named 'garnata' in the 13th century by the German theologian and philosopher Albertus Magnus (1193–1280), perhaps from the Latin *malum garnatum* ('pomegranate') because of their most frequent colour, or perhaps from *granum* ('grain') in reference to their shape. The garnet family also includes many minerals which in ancient times used to be called 'carbuncles' from the Latin *carbunculus* ('red-hot coal'). It is quite certain that Pliny the Elder used this term to describe the garnet almandine, for instance.

Garnets are among the most widespread minerals. The group comprises minerals of similar composition and structure, which mix with one another. They come in a

170   Almandine — Starkoč, near Čáslav (Czech Republic); actual size 7 x 4.5 cm

greater variety of colours than any other mineral. This is because the group consists of a large number of binary silicates of bivalent and trivalent elements which share isometric symmetry. They crystallise most frequently in the cubic system as rhombododecahedra or trapezohedra. Very often they form granular to massive clusters in the rocks. They have no cleavage, but often have distinct partings (especially almandine). Since garnets of different composition intermingle, a pure variety hardly ever exists.

In the natural kingdom, garnets develop under the most varied conditions, but always at high temperatures. Perfectly bounded crystals form in gneisses and mica schists, but also in phyllite, marble, serpentinites and granite pegmatites. As garnets are highly resistant to the effects of weathering, they often occur in alluvial deposits. Garnets often develop through contact of igneous rocks with other rocks. This is the origin of garnet rocks, which are contact rocks formed chiefly of garnet, pyroxenes and minerals with magnetite.

Pyrope is undoubtedly the most popular of the garnet family. It is also known as Czech, or Bohemian garnet because its most important deposits are in the central Bohemian highlands where the garnets have been collected since the end of the 16th century. This was when the largest Czech garnet was found. It was the size of a pigeon's egg and probably was held in the Prague collections of Emperor Rudolf II. At present it is shown as part of the treasures of the Saxon Kurfürst (electors of the Emperor). A garnet of such a size is exceptionally rare — even pyropes which are the size of a pea are very rare.

The parent rocks of pyrope are chiefly serpentinites and peridotites, but the most common occurrence is in alluvials. Pyrope usually forms dark fiery red grains of vitreous lustre. This is also the origin of its name, which is derived from the Greek *pyropos* ('fiery eyed'). The colouring is caused by the admixture of chromium and iron.

The most noted deposits are, apart from the central Bohemian highlands, the diamond mines in Kimberley (South Africa), in Arizona (USA), and in the kimberlites on the diamond deposits in Yakutskaya (eastern Siberia). Garnets are often named after the locality where they are found, such as the Czech (Bohemian) garnet, 'Cape ruby' or 'Arizona ruby'. Smaller deposits are in Australia, at Makonde in Tanzania, and in Brazil. The light pink-red to faintly violet mixtures of pyrope and almandine are called rhodolites and occur in California.

Czech garnets are today much sought after as gemstones. They owe their popularity to their beautiful colouring and lustre, which are further enhanced by cutting and polishing. However, Czech garnets seldom reach a large size; the 'Cape rubies', for example, are much larger.

Garnets which have the almandine composition are the most abundant. They are also the chief component of the so-called common garnet. **Almandine** received its name from the location of its first discovery — the surroundings of the ancient city of Alabanda in what is now south-west Turkey, where it was mined in the past. At that time, almandines with a violet hue, were particularly valued. Among all the garnets, almandine is the one which has been used as a precious stone for the longest time.

Schists are the most common parent rock of almandines. Almandine crystals are usually fairly large (in comparison with pyrope for example) and frequently perfectly bounded. They often retain their high gem quality even when they are large. Because, of this, there are quite a few well known cut almandines, exceptional in size and perfectly coloured. The largest one is in the collection of the Smithsonian Institution in Washington. This 175-carat asteric almandine from the state of Idaho has been cut to a lenticular shape.

Almandine resembles pyrope in colour, but it is distinguishable by its violet or brownish hue. It is also usually paler than pyrope. The different hues are the result of different admixtures. Pure almandine is an exception. More frequently it contains some pyrope components, some spessartite, and often further admixtures. A violet hue, for example, is caused by the presence of iron and chromium.

The most important deposits of almandine of gemstone quality today occur in Sri Lanka, India, Australia, Madagascar, Brazil and the USA. The most noted European localities are in Tirol (Austria), near Čáslav (Czech Republic), and in Romania. Depending on the source of the major deposits, almandine is often referred to as 'Oriental garnet' or 'Tirolese garnet'. The best come from the gemstome alluvials in Sri Lanka (the 'Ceylon ruby'). In India, where there are numerous almandine deposits, large

171 Hessonite — Ala Piedmont (Italy); actual size of crystals 5 mm

172 Spessart-
ite — Tokovaya,
the Urals
(Russia); actual
size of crystals
8–9 mm

▷
173   Garnet
— Baia Sprie
(Romania);
actual size
6 x 4.5 cm

rounded crystals are found in alluvials. The Tirolese almandine crystals, intergrown into the grey-green slate, are often perfectly bounded and very beautiful; some specimens are as large as 5 cm or even more. Fairly recently, a new deposit of attractive almandine crystals has been discovered in Alaska, where they are intergrown into dark grey mica schists.

Andradite, another mineral in the garnet group, received its name from the Greek *andras*,used originally by the Greek philosopher, surgeon and natural scientist Theophrastus (372–287 BC); at that time the name applied to all the garnet family. Andradite is commonly massive to compact. It often occurs in 'skarn' deposits in association with magnetite, pyroxene hedenbergite or amphibole; it is also found in serpentinites. The gemstone varieties, mainly demantoid and melanite, are the most important.

The green demantoid is without doubt the most valuable garnet. It was first discovered in gold-bearing alluvia near Nizhni Tagil in the Urals (Russia) in the 1860s. In its parent rock it was found twenty years later by the banks of the nearby Bobrovka brook in the Systertsk district. Demantoid outshines all the other garnets in lustre and dispersive power (the ability to break up white into the colours of the spectrum) and in this it is similar to diamond. Its name is in fact derived from diamond. Its alternative name, topazolite, is applied because the mineral resembles topaz in colour. The emerald, light green or yellow-green colouring of demantoid is caused by the presence of chromium. The most recent discoveries of demantoids of gemstone quality are at Val Malenca in northern Italy and in Tanzania.

Melanite takes its name from the Greek *melas* ('black'). It is dark brown to black, which is caused by the presence of titanium and sodium. Melanite usually occurs in crystal form in volcanic rocks, such as phonolites. The main deposits are at Frascati near Rome, at Mount Vesuvius near Naples, and at Keiserstuhl in Germany. Melanite is generally used in the manufacture of jewellery.

Grossular is a garnet which was named after *Grossularia*, former botanical name for the gooseberry, because of its gooseberry colour. It occurs compact or crystallised, and forms at high temperatures at the points where granite magma rich in silicon dioxide is in contact with carbonate rocks; another process of its formation is through the action of limestone on high-aluminium rocks. The main deposits include the drainage basins of the Vilyui and Ural rivers in Russia. In several localities in South Africa compact grossular is found in a variety of colours (at Wollrütterskop for example).

Hessonite is basically a grossular variety rich in iron. The name comes from the Greek *esson* ('inferior'), for it is of less value than zircon, which it resembles. In the chief deposits of the gemstone varieties of hessonite, the placers of Sri Lanka, it occurs in association with hyacinth, a zircon variety for which it used to be mistaken.

Like grossular, hessonite is a typical contact mineral, occurring at the points of contact of igneous rocks and limestone. Large crystals of hessonite occur near Žulová in the Jeseníky mountains in the Czech part of Silesia, in Piemonte region in northern Italy, on the banks of the river Vilyui in Yakutskaya (Siberia), at Xalostoc in Mexico, and at Mudgee in New South Wales.

Spessartite is not as well known as those already mentioned. It was named after the locality of its first discovery — Spessart in Bavaria. It nearly always contains a smaller or larger admixture of almandine, so in colour it is extremely changeable. Usually it is yellow, orange, reddish, or brown; effects of weathering turn it dark to black. It usually occurs in crystal form.

Spessartite is chiefly found in granite pegmatites, granites, and other igneous rocks and its main deposits, apart from Aschaffenburg in Spessart in the Harz mountains, are in Sweden, at Miass and Tokovaya in the Urals, at Haddam in Connecticut (USA), Ampandramaika in Madagascar, and Sri Lanka. The transparent spessartite varieties are very popular precious stones.

Uvarovite is considered to be the most beautiful green precious stone. Found mainly in chromium deposits, it is rather a rare garnet. The most beautiful specimens of uvarovite come from serpentinites recovered at Syserts and Saranai in the Urals, where

174 Cut garnets. From top:
Almandine — India,
three Pyropes — central
Bohemian highlands
(Czech Republic);
Demantoid — Urals (Russia);
Almandine — India;
Spessartite — Madagascar;
Melanite — Vesuvius (Italy);
actual size of largest
almandine 32.4 x 18.6 mm

it occurs in association with demantoid. Other deposits are at Jordanów in Poland, the Texas mine in Pennsylvania (USA) and Makri in Turkey. Uvarovite crystals are so minute that they are hardly ever suitable for cutting and polishing.

The non-transparent combinations of different types of garnet are called common garnet. The colour differs according to the chemical composition. The main component is usually almandine or andradite, and the most common occurrence is in schists and gneisses.

Garnets are among the best abrasive and polishing materials, used also for the manufacture of abrasive paper. As an abrasive, garnet is superior to the harder quartz, for during use its shape is always sharp, which prolongs its abrasive efficiency.

Their hardness makes garnets, especially pyropes, highly suitable as bearings in fine instruments. The physical properties of pyrope, particularly its thermal conductivity and elasticity, are an advantage. Pyropes are particularly its suitable stones for very accurate clocks. Small grains of pyrope also serve as tare during weighing.

Zircon - *zirconium silicate*, $ZrSiO_4$

Tetragonal; H. 7.5; Sp. gr. 3.9–4.8 g/cm^3; commonly yellow-brown, brownish-yellow, red-brown to black, pale yellow to colourless; adamantine lustre, greasy on fracture; S. white

Zircon has a unique position among precious stones: its uses in the jewellery industry are not based on old tradition, as in te case of sapphire, ruby or spinel, for zircon was not fully utilised until the modern era and then mainly owing to its resemblance to diamond. Until that time, pure clear zircons had been used for jewellery purposes only

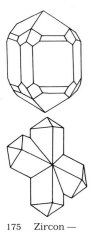

175 Zircon — Jizerská louka (Czech Republic); actual size of largest grain 13 mm

occasionally. They came onto the European markets under the name 'Matara diamonds', after the town of that name in Sri Lanka near which there are deposits of zircons. For a long time, everyone assumed they were diamonds.

It seems strange that at first even the beautiful yellow-red, highly lustrous zircon variety, hyacinth, was not more popular in Europe; it had been mined from days of old in rich alluvials in Sri Lanka. Hyacinth was examined in greater detail at the end of the 18th century. The element zirconium was then discovered; however, proof that the clear 'Matara diamonds' from Sri Lanka were the same mineral did not come until much later.

Zircon commonly occurs in tetragonal crystals or in grains embedded in rocks. Small amounts (a so-called accessory mineral) are frequently found in igneous rocks, especially in those rich in silicon dioxide and in alkaline metals such as potassium and sodium. Zircon occurs in substantial quantities chiefly in some syenites and pegmatites, in metamorphic rocks and in alluvials. Such secondary occurrences, especially in sandstones and gravels, are of the greatest practical use. Zircon is one of the most abundant heavy minerals in such deposits, because of its mechanical and chemical stability.

The main production of zircon is Travancore in India, where beach sands are recovered; zircon is their secondary, but important, product. This deposit is, of course, only important for industrial uses. The most noted deposits of zircon of gemstone quality are, apart from Sri Lanka, Miass in the Urals (Russia), Renfrew in Ontario (Canada), Henderson county in North Carolina (USA) and Cerro de Caldos in Brazil. The European deposits, for example in Tirol, the Rhineland and south-eastern Norway, rarely yield zircons of gemstone quality.

Zircon as a gemstone is particularly valued for its lustre, which is especially high in the transparent stones. However, the physical characteristics of zircon fluctuate considerably; this is why their lustre is sometimes adamantine but at other times only vitreous.

Zircon is extracted for the production of zirconium, and sometimes also for the production of radioactive elements which may be present in the mineral. Zirconium is used chiefly in the manufacture of refractory materials, in abrasives and in special types of glass. Today it is also used in nuclear reactors as a safeguard against corrosion by uranium. Clear zircon, hyacinth, and other coloured but transparent varieties of zircon are very popular as gemstones.

176   Chiastolite — Bimbowrie (Australia); actual size of large crystal 4 x 3 cm

Andalusite - *aluminium silicate*, Al_2SiO_5

Orthorhombic; H. 7.5; Sp. gr. 3.1–3.2 g/cm³; white, pink and variously coloured vitreous lustre; S. white

Andalusite was named after the area where deposits were first found — in Andalusia (at Almeria on the southern coast of Spain). Before true andalusite was discovered, its variety, chiastolite (name derived from resemblance to the Greek letter *khi*) was already known from the city of Santiago de Compostella, to which pilgrimages were often made. This variety was used for the manufacture of memorial objects, the so-called 'stone of the Cross'. Chiastolites are, basically, crystals of andalusite arranged in regular directions and filled with carbonaceous substances. Otherwise andalusite forms columnar or stalk-like crystals or stalky and leafy aggregates. It occurs in gneisses, in metamorphosed contact slates resembling phyllites (chiastolitic slates) and in pegmatites. In many deposits it is accompanied by staurolite or corundum. Industrially important deposits are in Kazakhstan and in California. The other most noted deposits are in Austria, at Murzinka in the Urals, in Brazil and in Bimbowrie in South Australia. Andalusite is used in the manufacture of refractory materials and special porcelains. The variety from Brazil is used as a less common precious gemstone.

The minerals disthene and sillimanite have the same chemical composition. Disthene is triclinic and sillimanite orthorhombic. Disthene received its name from

the Greek *di* ('double') and *sthenos* ('strength'), on account of its conspicuously different hardness in different directions. The hardness of its tabular crystals is 4–5 along the prism but 7 across. The blue variety is called kyanite, the white to grey variety rhaeticite. Sillimanite is commonly finely fibrous to acicular, and is coloured white. When mixed with quartz, it is called fibrolite.

177 Andalusite — Tyrol (Austria); actual size of large crystal 7.5 cm

Orthorhombic; H. 8; Sp. gr. 3.5–3.6 g/cm^3; clear or variably coloured, commonly yellowish to yellow, honey yellow, blue, pinkish, pink to violet; vitreous lustre; S. white

Topaz is one of the longest known gemstones, already popular in ancient times. In those days when only the Old World deposits were known, it was highly prized. Later, when rich deposits yielding magnificent stones of substantial size were found in America, interest in topaz fell considerably. Only a few of the coloured topaz varieties have remained popular, mainly the honey-blonde, pink and (until recently) blue stones. This unfavourable change in the valuation of topaz was chiefly caused by the discovery of the largest ever topaz deposits in Brazil.

Topaz most probably received its name from the island of Topazos in the Red Sea, because in ancient times it was confused with the chrysolite variety of olivine, found on the island. Some mineralogists believe the name was derived from the Sanskrit word *tapas* ('fire'). Many ornamental stones of yellow colour were called *topazus* (yellowish olivines for instance) in ancient times, whereas the true yellow topaz was called *chrysolithos* ('gold stones'). Only when the science of mineralogy became established was topaz distinguished from chrysolite, the beautiful yellowish-green variety of olivine.

Topaz occurs most often completely colourless, or white, or grey. Small admixtures of some metals, however, give the mineral various shades. The common yellowish hue, for instance, is caused by a small admixture of chromium, the bluish colour by traces of iron in which the oxidation number is 3, or by exposure to radioactive radiation. A yellow-red colour is also typical, but the pink colouring of the Brazilian topaz is much rarer.

Topaz crystals are usually columnar, mostly bounded by prisms with multiple-faced pyramidal endings. In other instances the crystals terminate with smooth basal

178   Topaz — Adun Chilon, Siberia (Russia); actual size 9 x 6 cm

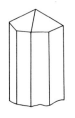

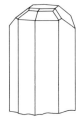

surfaces, on which the characteristics etchings often arise. The prism faces are frequently vertically striated and display a prominent vitreous lustre. Even large crystals are usually transparent. Topazes from various deposits exhibit interesting surface irregularities, which occur through gradual dissolution.

Topazes have distinct endings only at one end, because the crystals usually grow upwards. They have a perfect cleavage. Many crystals are surprisingly large.

In the American Natural Science Museum in New York there is a perfectly bounded crystal from Minas Gerais, Brazil, which weighs 300 kg and measures 80 x 60 x 60 cm. The museum of the Mineralogical Institute in Florence has a pink crystal from the same deposit weighing 150 kg. The topaz mines in Brazil boast of a find of a yellow crystal, broken into three pieces, which jointly weigh 140 kg. A giant blue topaz from Murzinka in the Urals is on show in the Mining College museum in St. Petersburg.

The most famous cut and polished topaz is a 1,680-carat stone called 'Braganza', which was first mistaken for diamond. It is set in the Portuguese royal crown. This topaz was found in 1740 at Ouro Prêto in Brazil. The largest cut and polished topazes are held in the collections of the Smithsonian Institution in Washington, and they all come from Brazil. The largest yellowish topaz weighs 7,725 carats, blue 3,273 carats, and yellow-green 1,469 carats. The most renowned topaz collection is among the treasures of *Das grüne Gewölbe* in Dresden, Germany. It consists of many large topaz stones set in various pieces of jewellery, and some unset stones. Originally even uncut topazes were in this collection.

Topaz occurs more frequently in granular or columnar form than in crystallised form. Such topaz stones are called pycnites (from the Greek *pyknos*, 'fat'). Pycnites are commonly non-transparent, usually yellowish, greenish or pinkish, and because of this they cannot be worked as gemstones.

Topaz is a characteristic druse mineral, found in cavities of some granites, especially those of the coarse-grained type (pegmatites). It is also often found in cassiterite veins. In alluvials topaz occurs as a subsidiary mineral.

There are many famous deposits of topaz, some of which yield typically coloured varieties. The best known occurrences are in Brazil, where topaz is found mainly in the state of Minas Gerais in two separate localities: the north-east part of the state and in the vicinity of its capital, Ouro Prêto. The clear colourless topazes from the north-eastern part of Minas Gerais were first recovered from the gemstone placers as pebbles called *pingos d'agoa* ('drops of water'); primary deposits were later discovered in pegmatite veins in horizons of mica schists and gneisses. The rich yellow and yellow-red

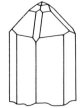

179 Cut topaz — Brazil; actual size of larger stone: 29.8 mm across, weight 164.7 carat

180 Cut topaz — Brazil; actual size
43.9 x 30.6 mm; weight 197 carat

181 Cut topaz — Brazil; actual size
66.9 x 59.4 mm; weight 1,463 carat

topazes from the vicinity of Ouro Prêto were discovered in 1760 in weathered pegmatite veins which intruded into clay slates. Topaz is usually accompanied by clear quartz (rock crystal), smoky quartz, haematite, tourmaline and other minerals. Other occurrences are at Villa Rica in the state of Rio Grande do Sul, Brazil, again in pegmatites.

Other famous deposits which yield topaz crystals which excel in size and beauty and are varied in colour, are in Russia. They are often accompanied by beryl. The transparent, faintly blue crystals come chiefly from Murzinka in the Urals (near Ekaterinburg). They occur in association with smoky quartz, feldspar and lepidolite in granite cavities. Miass, in the Urals, is noted for a colourless topaz variety, the Adun-Chilon Mountains in Siberia for yellowish crystals, and Urulga in the Transbaikal region for the yellowy wine-coloured crystals. These are particularly large crystals. The Ukraine also has a number of new deposits where large crystals occur, such as at Volodar near Zhitomir, west of Kiev.

Of the other world deposits, the clear crystals of Japan are the most important, then the famous gemstone placers of Sri Lanka which yield the clear, yellow and pale green topazes. The Gilgit deposit in northern Pakistan, where blue topaz prevails, has been gaining increasing importance in recent years. Australia and North America also have topaz deposits, but these are not as rich as those already mentioned. The most noted European deposit of topaz is at Schneckenstein in the Erzgebirge in Saxony (Germany), but it no longer has any practical significance. The occurrence of pycnite in the cassiterite veins of the Erzgebirge near Zinnwald in Germany and Cínovec in the Czech Republic are of mineralogical interest.

Topaz's primary use is as a gemstone. It remains one of the most popular stones, though its price is lower now than in the past. Even the price of the blue topazes has fallen because it is possible at present to make large quantities of blue stones from the cheap colourless topaz. Topaz is appreciated for its hardness, transparency, pleasant colours and hues, and its purity as a mineral. The excellent cleavage enables the material to be easily divided but makes the process of grinding all the harder. Some varieties tend to fade in sunlight, especially the richly coloured ones. This was known long ago, but not until much more recently was it proved that it is not the light but the warmth of the sun's rays which cause the change in colours. From that time on jewellers began changing the colour of topaz artificially by heating it. It is possible, for instance, to alter the Brazilian rich yellow or yellow-red topaz to a rose-red stone with a high refractive index and strong pleochroism.

In exceptional cases clear topaz is used as a raw material for the manufacture of special optical lenses. Topaz also has industrial uses as abrasive powder. The making of synthetic topaz is so far only of theoretical, and not of practical importance. Synthetic corundum, and sometimes also spinel, are used to imitate topaz. The most common topaz imitations are the so-called Spanish, Ural and Madeira topazes which are, in reality, rich yellow to yellow-orange citrines, obtained by the firing of amethyst.

Staurolite - *complex basic silicate of iron and aluminium*, $Al_9Fe(O_3)(OH)(SiO_4)_2$

Orthorhombic; H. 7–7.5; Sp. gr. 3.7–3.8 g/cm^3; brown, red-brown to black-brown; dull vitreous lustre, greasy on fracture; S. colourless

Staurolite was so named from the Greek *stauros* ('cross') and *lithos* ('stone'), because its crystals form twins which are intergrown in cross-like fashion. This is why it was also called *lapis crucifix* and why the twinned crystals were often worn as amulets. The most beautiful specimens came together with kyanite from the pale mica schists of Monte Campione near Faido and from Lago Ritone in the Ticino canton in Switzerland. They were sold under the name *Baseler Taufsteine* (Basle baptismal stones).

It is interesting to note that individual columnar crystals are rarer than the interpenetrated twins. They occur embedded in schists, especially mica schists and metamorphic (contact) rocks of sedimentary origin. Sometimes staurolite appears as a rock-forming mineral.

The main deposits include the St. Gotthard pass (Monte Campione) and Lago Ritone in Switzerland, Fannin county in Georgia and Lisbon and Franconia in New Hampshire, USA, Sanarka near Orenburg in the Urals in Russia (loose crystals in alluvials), Passeyr and Sterzing in Tirol, St. Redegund in Styria (Austria), Aschaffenburg in Bavaria (Germany), Quimper in Brittany (France), Branná and Hrubý Jeseník (Czech

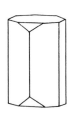

182 Staurolite —
Quimper (France);
actual size of crystals
up to 1 cm

Republic). Large staurolite crystals have recently been found in the Gorob mine in Namibia and, particularly, at Ducktown in Tennessee (USA).

Staurolite in which iron is replaced by cobalt and magnesium is called lusakite. It is found in Lusaka, Zambia, where it occurs as an important rock-forming mineral (representing up to 30 per cent of the rock). Lusakite is extracted as blue pigment from the Zambian deposit.

Titanite - *silicate of titanium and calcium*, $CaTiSiO_5$

Monoclinic; H. 5–5.5; Sp. gr. 3.4–3.6 g/cm^3; commonly yellowish, greenish, yellow, brown, brown-red to reddish; strong to adamantine lustre; S. colourless

Titanite crystallises in columnar, tabular, or acicular form; less commonly it occurs in lumps or forms granular and dish-shaped aggregates. Its varieties have been given various names. Sphene is a transparent variety, which forms wedge-shaped crystals (the name in Greek means 'wedge'). Titanite crystals, especially those of the sphene variety, most frequently occur in cracks of rocks such as crystalline schists, and are characteristic of what is called 'Alpine paragenesis'. As a secondary part of rocks, titanite occurs in pegmatite veins permeating crystalline limestones, in granodiorites, syenites and allied igneous rocks. Titanite, however, may also occur even in other rocks, such as phonolite and greenstone.

The main deposits of titanite are in the vicinity of St. Gotthard in the Swiss Alps, near

183   Titanite — Ofenhorn (Switzerland); actual size of crystals up to 1 cm

184 Titanite —
St Gotthard
(Switzerland);
actual size of
crystals 2 cm

Akhmatovsk in the Urals and in the Khibiny massif on the Kola peninsula in northern Russia, where titanite occurs in basic syenites (with a poor content of silicon dioxide). In the Khibiny mountains on the Kola peninsula, titanite is recovered as a by-product during the mining of apatites. Other noted deposits of titanite are near Kragerö in Norway, in the Plauen valley near Dresden in Germany, near Čáslav (Czech Republic), in the Tilly Foster Iron Mine in the state of New York and in some other places.

Titanite, when found in larger quantities, is an important titanium ore (it contains up to 24.5 per cent metal). Titanium is added to steels (ferro-titanium alloys), which are very resilient, especially against acids. Compounds of titanium are used as yellow and yellow-red glazes in the ceramic industry, in the manufacture of synthetic fibres and in the textile industry. Titanium dioxide is the basic ingredient of 'titanium white' (a brilliant white paint). Titanium itself is noted for its very low weight, resistance to corrosion, and hardness. In some deposits titanite is also a valuable source of rare earths which are often admixed in titanite.

Titanites are seldom used as gemstones, though attractively coloured and perfectly transparent titanites are sometimes cut and polished.

Hemimorphite - *hydrous basic zinc silicate*, $Zn_4(OH)_2Si_2O_7 \cdot H_2O$

Orthorhombic; H. 5; Sp. gr. 3.3–3.5 g/cm³; commonly colourless to clear, or yellow to brown; strong vitreous lustre; S. colourless

Hemimorphite has been found in the upper parts of the veins of zinc and lead ores, usually associated with smithsonite with which it was often confused, both minerals being classed under the same name 'calamine'. In the second half of the 18th century it was discovered that there were two different minerals, one a zinc carbonate, the other a zinc silicate.

The silicate was the rarer of the two, and was named hemimorphite on account of the hemimorph development of its crystals. This unusual form, which exists in only a few minerals, means that the crystals are terminated by dissimilar faces. Hemimorphite most commonly forms crystalline crusts and coatings and also massive, granular, globose and reniform aggregates, and concentrically layered, finely stalk-shaped, fibrous or stalactitic, rarely fan-shaped clusters of crystals.

Hemimorphite most frequently occurs as the product of the oxidation of the upper parts of sphalerite, accompanied by other secondary minerals which form the so-called 'iron cap'. Less frequently it originates by the process of metasomatism, that is by the gradual replacement of the readily soluble limestone with less soluble substances from the solutions. In deposits of this type hemimorphite usually occurs in association with sphalerite and galena.

Regions on the Belgian-German border are well known for their deposits of hemimorphite deposits of metasomatic origin, especially Vieille Montagne in Belgium and Aachen in Germany. Other deposits are near Tarnowice in Upper Silesia (Poland), near Phoenixville (Pennsylvania) and in a number of places in northern Africa. Hemimorphite is also found at Nerchinsk in Siberia, Rabelj in Slovenia, and Bleiberg in Carinthia (Austria). Hemimorphite is an important ore of zinc and contains up to 54.2 per cent metal.

185   Hemimorphite — Nerchinsk, Siberia (Russia); actual size of detail 7 x 6 cm

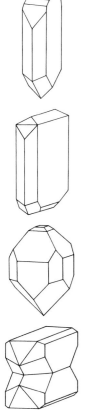

186   Epidote — Knappenwand, Salzburg (Austria); actual length of largest crystal 8 cm

Epidote - *very complex basic alumino-silicate of calcium and iron*

Monoclinic; H. 6–7; Sp. gr. 3.3–3.5 g/cm³; commonly greenish, pale green, brownish-green to black, paler if containing less iron; vitreous lustre; S. grey

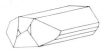

Epidote was given the name from the Greek *epidosis* ('addition'), because for a long time it had been mistaken for tourmaline and because its identification meant an addition to the mineral system.

The French mineralogist and crystallographer René Justin Haüy was the first to distinguish the two minerals in 1801. It is also known under the name pistacite for its green colour resembling the pistachio plant.

Epidote forms multiple-faced columnar crystals, stalky, granular and compact aggregates, coatings and crusts. Sometimes epidote forms separate rocks, called epidosites. Crystallised epidote is green, massive varieties and epidosites are yellow-green to yellow. Epidote is another contact mineral, but occurs in other metamorphic rocks as well, which have originated under low temperatures and high pressures (low-iron epidotes), especially in schists and skarns. It is fairly abundant. Epidosites form nests and fillings in amphibolites.

The main deposits are in Knappenwand in Sulzbachtal (Salzburg, Austria), Sobotín in the Hrubý Jeseník (Czech Republic), Kowary in the Polish part of Silesia, Akhmatovsk in Russia, Lake Superior in North America, and Sulzer in Prince of Wales Island off Alaska. As it lacks hardness and a distinct colour, it is little used as a precious stone. Usually only the dark green epidotes are cut and polished, for example those from Salzburg and Sri Lanka. It has no other practical significance. Some beautifully crystallised specimens, chiefly from Knappenwand, are greatly desired by collectors.

Epidote which contains the rare-earth elements is called orthite (from the Greek *orthos*, 'straight', on account of the shape of the crystals). It occurs in the form of black or brownish grains with a resinous lustre, embedded in granites and pegmatites.

Zoisite - *basic silicate of calcium and aluminium*, $Ca_2Al_3OH(SiO_4)_3$

Orthorhombic; H. 6; Sp. gr. 3.2–3.4 g/cm³; grey-white, greenish, brownish, reddish (thulite), rarely blue (tanzanite); vitreous lustre, pearly on cleavage surfaces; S. colourless

Zoisite aroused no great interest until 1967. It was then that a tailor, Manuel d'Souza, found by chance a beautifully coloured blue gemstone near his home town of Arusha, south-west of Kilimanjaro (Tanzania). This discovery stirred great interest worldwide and the mineral was called 'the Blue Treasure of Africa'. It was named tanzanite, after the country of its discovery, by the noted jewellers Tiffany of New York, keenly interested in this exceptionally beautiful stone.

Specialists at the German society for precious stones in Idar-Oberstein in Germany, where the mineral was brought for cutting and polishing, at last gave the stone its exact

187 Zoisite —
Zermatt
(Switzerland);
actual size of
crystals 4 cm

188   Vesuvianite — Egg (Norway); actual size of crystals 1.5 cm

identity. They discovered that tanzanite was a variety of zoisite, normally a rather inconspicuous mineral of usually greyish or brownish colouring. The blue colour of tanzanite is obviously caused by a large proportion of strontium. It was unambiguously ascertained that there is no reason to consider tanzanite as a new mineral in the true sense of the word, although it is a most interesting stone. The blue variety of zoisite was, until then, quite unknown. It is said that Elizabeth Taylor, the American film star, owns one of the most beautiful pieces of tanzanite jewellery — a necklace with five large tanzanite stones.

The mineral zoisite (named after a collector, Sigmund Zois von Edelstein, who financed mineral-collecting expeditions, during one of which zoisite was discovered) commonly forms massive striated aggregates with a coarse or fine stalk-like to fibrous structure. It seldom occurs in the crystal form. The pink variety, coloured by the presence of manganese, is called thulite after Thule, the ancient name for Norway, where thulite is found. Zoisite occurs in the cracks and deep igneous rocks, where it forms a secondary mineral through alteration of the original minerals of which the rock is composed, and in contact limestones.

The main zoisite deposits are at Zermatt in Switzerland, Norway, Gefries in Germany, Borovina near Třebíč (Czech Republic), and Saualpe in Carinthia (Austria), and in California and Tennessee (USA).

The pink Norwegian thulite has been used for a long time for jewellery purposes; the Californian grey-green zoisite has also been used to a certain extent in recent years, though, generally, they have no wide use. Tanzanite is a better gemstone than the other varieties. It is popular chiefly for its blue colouring, whose richness is further accentuated by firing the stone. Though tanzanite's refractive index is lower than that of the normal common zoisite, it is still rather high, similar to corundum, which raises its gemstone quality, just as the low double-refraction does. However, its low hardness and obvious cleavage are a disadvantage.

Tanzanite has climbed into the class of exceptionally precious stones and is valued as such. Its price is unlikely to fall as rumours are circulating that its only deposit is almost exhausted. The largest tanzanite found to date weighs 126 carats.

Vesuvianite - *highly compex basic silicate of calcium, magnesium and aluminium, with iron*

Tetragonal; H. 6.5; Sp. gr. 3.27–3.45 g/cm³; commonly green-brown, brown or green, variably shaded; vitreous lustre, greasy on fracture; S. colourless

Vesuvianite could be called the mineral of many names. The main name was given to it from the site of its occurrence in Italy, Vesuvius volcano near Naples, where it is found in igneous rocks. Another name, idocrase, is derived from the Greek *idos* ('likeness') and *krasis* ('composition'), for this mineral has a similar composition to some garnets and is often mistaken for them.

A number of other names are based on the various localities of its deposits. For example, the name egeran is derived from the German name of Cheb (Czech Republic) where it was discovered. The nearby deposits at Hazlov are world famous; the stone occurs there in association with the hessonite variety of garnet and with wollastonite. The variety found at Hazlov is always brown and has a coarsely acicular structure and the name egeran is sometimes applied to all brown or acicular varieties. The poet and dramatist Goethe, who often stayed in Bohemia, was so taken with the beauty of this stone that he composed a poem about it. Vilyuite, another name for vesuvianite, comes from the mineral's occurrence on the banks of the river Vilyui in eastern Siberia, and the name californite from California.

For quite a while, vesuvianite was mistaken for tourmaline because of its external characteristics, and also for olivine, topaz or garnet. The eventual recognition of vesuvianite as a separate mineral was by Abraham Gottlob Werner, the mineralogist from Freiberg, who named it vesuvianite.At the same time, vesuvianite was identified as a highly complex silicate. Its chemical formula can give only an approximate composition, for this mineral often contains admixtures of other elements, particularly manganese, chromium and berylium.

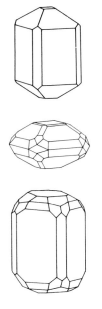

189 Vesuvianite — Vesuvius (Italy); actual size of crystals up to 2 cm

Vesuvianite forms many-faced columnar crystals or elongated needle-shaped, granular or compact aggregates, and occasionally pyramidal crystals. The crystals are rather fragile, usually only translucent and non-transparent. Different varieties are differently coloured; for example, egeran is brown, californite green, vilyuite black-green. The yellow variety was called xantite and the pale blue variety cyprine.A typical mineral of limestone and dolomite in contact with igneous rocks, it occurs there in association with other contact minerals, mainly silicates of calcium. Less frequently it is found in cracks of crystalline schists.

From the many localities of vesuvianite's occurrence, the following are of importance, apart from those already mentioned: Göpfersgrün in Germany, Arendal, Kristiansand and Oslo in Norway, Monzoni near Predazzo in the Italian Dolomites, Cziklov in Romania, Bludov near Šumperk (Czech Republic), the Akhmatov mine in the Urals (Russia). The most important deposits are in America. Californites are found in Siskiyou county and Riverside in California. Imperfect crystals, bipyramidally developed, occur in gigantic sizes of up to 30 cm in length in Magnet Cove in Arkansas. Better-formed crystals (up to 8 cm in size) come from Ludwig in Nevada. Really perfect crystals are found on contacts of limestones at Scratch Gravel in Montana and near Sanford (York county) in Maine. Collectors also frequent deposits in Mexico and Canada. Columnar crystals from the deposits at Xalostoc and by Lake Jaco in Chihuahua province in Mexico are well known among collectors. Gemstone varieties of vesuvianite come from Brazil and, particularly, from Kenya. Beautifully coloured contact rocks with vesuvianite are often cut and polished.

Prehnite - *complex basic silicate of calcium and aluminium,*

$$Ca_2Al_2(OH)_2Si_3O_{10}$$

Orthorhombic; H 6–6.5; Sp. gr. 2.8–3.0 g/cm³; commonly green-white; vitreous lustre; S. white

190   Prehnite — Haslach (Germany); actual size of aggregates up to 1 cm

191 Prehnite —
Scotland; actual size
of detail 7 x 6 cm

Prehnite was first brought to Europe by a Dutch colonel from the Cape of Good Hope in 1783. On account of the radiating varied shades, the stone was taken to be either an emerald variety or olivine, and was called accordingly either 'capemerald' or 'capchry-solite'. Later, when the same stones were found in European deposits, it was thought to be zeolite. Because of its appearance, it was referred to as *gelber Strahlzeolit* ('yellow radiating zeolite'). Not until 1789 was it established as a distinct mineral by the German mineralogist and geologist Abraham Gottlob Werner, a professor at the Mining Academy of Freiberg in Saxony.

Prehnite crystallises in tabular form, often rounded and clustered in fan-like or radial groupings. It occurs as a secondary mineral of aluminium-calcium silicates, chiefly feldspars. Found most commonly in the druse cavities of rocks, such as amphibolites and other crystalline schists, it is often accompanied by other secondary drusal minerals, like natriumalumosilicate analcite and natrolite. The main deposits include Le Bourg-d'Oisans, near Grenoble, in the French Alps, Scotland, Italy, Markovice (Czech Republic), Paterson, New Jersey (USA), and Peru. Prehnite is occasionally used as a gemstone, cut into the cabochon shape.

Bavenite (named after the Baveno deposit in Italy) resembles prehnite but is far rarer. It is an orthorhombic complex basic silicate of beryllium, aluminium and calcium. It occurs in radiating crystal sheafs composed of fine white needles. Generally it originates through the decomposition of beryllium.

Benitoite - *barium titanium silicate*, BaTi(SiO₃)₃

Rhombohedral; H 6.5; Sp. gr. 3.7 g/cm³; blue, sometimes with violet shades, less commonly colourless; vitreous lustre; S. colourless

Benitoite, so named after its one and only major deposit at San Benito, near Mount Diablo, (east of San Francisco). For a long time it was mistaken for sapphire. In 1907, however, it was identified by the American mineralogist Landerback as a new mineral. It is found in metamorphosed serpentinites, which are chiefly composed of the sodium-magnesium amphibole crossite, and impregnated with cryptocrystalline natrolite. Benitoite is found in its parent rock on the walls of fissures, in association with rare minerals, such as the black neptunite (silicate of titanium, iron and sodium) and the tiny orange-brown crystals of jaquinite (complex silicate of sodium, calcium, titanium and iron).

Soon after being discovered, benitoite became highly prized as a gemstone. This is understandable, because it has a very high lustre, higher even than sapphire, and an exquisite blue colour, for which it was also aptly named 'the heavenly stone'. However, cutting and polishing presented difficulties. Benitoite crystals happen to show strong pleochroism, which means that they have different colours when light falls on them from different directions. They are richly blue in the direction of the main crystal axis, but in the perpendicular direction to the axis they are almost colourless. The occurrence of benitoite crystals in cracks of crystalline schists is very rare, unable to support a wider practical use of the mineral as a gemstone. Its value is very high, especially as its crystals are not commonly large. The largest crystal found to date weighed 7 carats.

192   Benitoite — Benito county, California (USA); actual size of crystals 14 mm

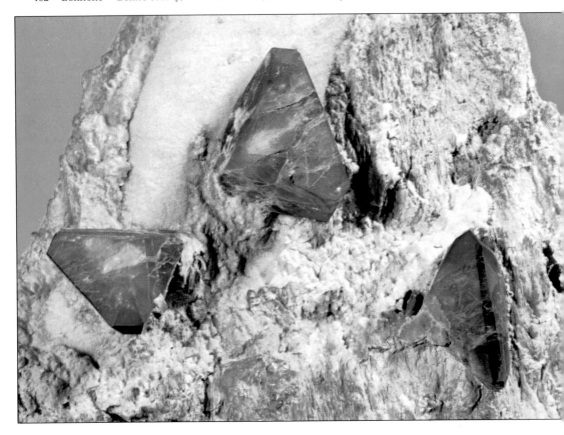

193 Aquamarine — Adun Chilon, Siberia (Russia); actual length of crystal 9 cm

194 Morganite — Pala, California (USA); actual size 15 x 12 cm

Beryl - *beryllium-aluminium silicate*, $Al_2Be_3(SiO_3)_6$

Hexagonal; H. 7.5–8; Sp. gr. 2.63–2.80 g/cm³; commonly greenish or differently coloured, for example, yellow to greenish-yellow (heliodor), green-blue (aquamarine), pink (morganite, vorobevite), green (emerald), occasionally colourless (goshenite); vitreous lustre; S. white

Beryl and its exquisitely colourful varieties, especially the emerald, have been widely used from time immemorial. It is said that Cleopatra had an emerald engraved with her own picture. The large Egyptian emerald mines were being worked during Cleopatra's time – but long before this they had been mined for the ancient Pharaohs (1650 BC). The ancient Romans searched for emeralds in Egypt later, then the Arabs and, later still, the Turks.

It is believed that the Peruvians worshipped an emerald as big as an ostrich egg. In today's Colombia, emeralds were recovered long before the appearance of the Spaniards, who took possession of the mines in 1537. In the Natural History Museum of Vienna there is a beautiful druse of emerald crystals 18 x 13 cm in size. It is said they belonged to Montezuma who was the Aztec emperor from 1502–1520. The druse found in the treasures of *Das grüne Gewölbe* in Dresden comes from the Prague collections of Rudolf II, who was Austrian emperor in 1576–1612. In the sanctuary of the Buddhist temple in Kandy, Sri Lanka, there is an ancient statuette of Buddha carved from a single piece of the gem.

A large worked emerald, perhaps the largest emerald known, is kept in the Art History Museum in Vienna: worked into the shape of a vase, it is 10 cm tall and weighs 2,681 carats. The largest world collection of emerald is probably in the treasure of the Turkish sultans in the Topkapi palace in Istanbul; these stones come from the deposits in Upper Egypt (Nubia). Many beautiful Colombian emeralds are in a number of churches all over Spain.

Emerald is a vivid green variety of beryl, and owes its colouring to the admixture of chromic oxide. But beryl has many other colour varieties apart from emerald, and many of them have been used as gemstones from time immemorial. These include, first of all, the pale blue aquamarine, the yellow to yellow-green and perfectly transparent golden beryl or heliodor, the pink morganite and vorobevite, whose colour is caused by the admixture of the rare element, caesium. Bixbite, the deep crimson beryl, is a much

195 Cut green beryls; actual size of larger stone 51.8 x 41.8 mm, weight 421 carat

sought-after rarity. The colourless goshenite, chemically the purest variety of beryl, is not of any particularly high value as a gemstone. Common beryl, which is non-transparent and has no use as a gemstone, occurs abundantly in the mineral world.

Beryl most commonly forms simple, prismatic hexagons, often elongated and columnar, more rarely thickly tabular. Sometimes the crystals reach several metres in length. In Maine (USA) crystals were found measuring up to 6 m and weighing as much as 1.5 tonnes. Low faces of hexagonal bipyramids may also occur on beryl crystals but this is not very common. It is interesting to note that the closer to gemstone quality, the higher is the number of crystal faces in beryl. To be able to rise and develop, gemstone varieties need undisturbed conditions for crystallisation and a regular supply of constituent particles with no impurities; complex faces can develop on crystals which have such good conditions during their growth. Beryl is often found in druses of columnar crystals; it may also be massive.

Beryl most frequently occurs embedded in coarse-grained granites, called pegmatites, or in rocks of a similar origin. The best examples of emeralds come from limestones and mica schists. The most beautiful aquamarines come from some screes and alluvial deposits, which are formed by the weathering of their parent rock, the coarse-grained granites. Other coloured varieties of beryl are of a similar origin; only bixbites occur in cracks of hydrothermally transformed ryolites in western Utah (USA). Beryls may also occur in greisens with tin and tungsten ores but such cases are not very common.

The most noted emerald deposits were in the region south of El Kassir in Nubia (south-ern Egypt), from where come all the ancient emeralds, and also the sultans' stones (green is the Prophet's colour). These mines are now deserted. The most beautiful specimens of emeralds are found now in the vicinity of Musso, Colombia, where the currently worked deposit of this stone is the largest in the world today. The Urals boast of extensive deposits, and the biggest emerald crystals are those from Transvaal,

196 Cut aquamarines — Brazil; actual size of largest stone 68.5 x 55.8 mm, weight 990.6 carat

South Africa. Production has been rapidly growing in the Brazilian state of Bahia in recent years, particularly in the Carnaiba deposit. The Carnaiba emeralds usually have a bluish hue. The best European deposit is at Habachtal in Tyrol, Austria.

Magnificent examples of aquamarine come from Brazil, particularly from near Governador Valadares in the state of Minas Gerais, and also from Russia, including Adun-Chilon near Nerchinsk in Siberia and Murzinka in the Urals, where the stone occurs in pegmatites and granites. New deposits have recently been discovered at Gilgit (Pakistan) and in Ukrainian pegmatites.

The southern Brazilian deposits are probably the most famous and richest in the world; they yield fairly frequently large aquamarine crystals of gem quality, most of them of pale blue colour. In 1910 a greenblue, perfectly clear aquamarine was found in the local pegmatites. It was nearly 0.5 m long and weighed over 110 kg (and was sold for US$25,000). The maxaxite variety is particularly highly prized; these deep blue aquamarines are so coloured by the admixture of boron. They were called after Maxaxa in the state of Minas Gerais, where they were discovered. The Minas Gerais deposits yield, apart from maxaxite, exquisite specimens of all the other coloured varieties of beryl of gem quality.

The Minas Gerais deposits of other gem-quality coloured varieties of beryl, particularly morganites and heliodors, include those in the vicinity of the towns of Teófilo Otôni, Diamantina and Governador Valadares. Deposits in the Rio Piauí area were famous mainly between the two World Wars.

The largest ground aquamarine (1,000 carats) is in the Smithsonian Institution in Washington. The National Museum in Prague has a pale blue aquamarine weighing 988 carats in its collection. A green aquamarine in the British Museum in London weighs 875 carats. All these large stones originate from Brazil, as do the stones in the German Precious Stone Museum at Idar-Oberstein and in the Natural History Museum in Paris. The largest existing private collection of aquamarines is in the USA. It consists of thirty large stones, including aquamarines and cut and polished specimens of other coloured varieties of beryl.

The value of aquamarine stones is nowhere near as high as that of emeralds. This applies also to the differently coloured gem varieties of beryl, though these are stones of exceptional beauty and have been much sought after in recent years, especially in some countries. There is one exception to this evaluation: some of the rare, richly grass-green beryls, whose colour (caused by factors other than an admixture of boron) differs from the colour of emerald.

The most important deposits of the coloured varieties of beryl are at Pala in California (mainly pink beryls) and Marahitra in Madagascar (morganites, heliodors and

198 Cordierite
— Madagascar;
actual size
up to 2.5 cm

aquamarines, and often transitions between these two). Another Madagascar deposit, at Antsirabé south of Antananarivo, is of similar nature.

Beryl is not only a prized gemstone, but also virtually the only raw material for the manufacture of one of the lightest metals, beryllium, used in the production of alloys. Pure beryl contains up to 14 per cent beryllium.

Cordierite - *aluminosilicate of magnesium*, $Mg_2Al_4Si_5O_{18}$

Orthorhombic; H. 7–7.5; Sp. gr. 2.6 g/cm³; commonly brown-blue, yellowish, brown-green, grey-blue, blue to violet, very strongly pleochroic (sometimes even to the naked eye); greasy to vitreous lustre; S. colourless

Cordierite was defined as a distinct mineral in 1813 and named after Louis Cordier, a French mineralogist and geologist, who was the first to describe it with accuracy in 1809. Long before this, cordierite was known and sought after as a gemstone, chiefly in Sri Lanka, where it was considered to be a sapphire variety. The dark cordierites, which resemble sapphires most closely, were called Luchssaphir ('sly sapphire') in Germany for a long time. The lighter shades of cordierite were sold in Sri Lanka under the name of 'water sapphires'. Of the many other names bestowed upon this mineral, it is worth mentioning dichroite (dual-coloured), which is distinctly pleochroic.

Cordierite occurs in the form of grains, short columnar crystals, or in massive form. It is comparatively common, especially in gneisses of sedimentary origin (paragneisses). With the effects of weathering it changes into various mica varieties. The main deposits are in Bodenmais in Bavaria, the surroundings of Murzinka in the Urals (Russia), Haddam in Connecticut (USA), Japan, and Sri Lanka. Cordierite crystals from Bodenmais are, as a rule, partially altered and reach a length of 4 cm. Crystals found at Orijarvi in Finland have not gone through the process of transformation and are up to 5 cm long. At Kragerö in Norway cordierite forms impressive vitreous masses of substantial dimensions. They are permeated with inclusions of red haematite. The best gemstone material today comes from Madagascar; however, it is not used very widely.

Imperfect crystals up to 20 cm in size were found at Dolní Bory near Velké Meziříčí in the Czech Republic and were taken for cordierite until 1968 when it was found that they were a ferrous analogy of cordierite, $Fe_2Al_4Si_5O_{18}$, and the new mineral was named sekaninaite after the Czech mineralogist, Josef Sekanina. Apart from brazilianite and bukovskyite, sekaninaite is probably the only newly discovered mineral which appears in fairly substantial amounts and therefore has great interest for collectors. Both cordierite and sekaninaite tend, through the weathering processes, to alter into micaceous pseudomorphs in which muscovite prevails, which are often called pinite or gigantolite.

Dioptase - *hydrous silicate of copper,* $Cu_3(SiO_3)_6.6H_2O$

Rhombohedral; H. 5; Sp. gr. 3.4 g/cm^3; green; vitreous lustre; S. green

Dioptase was first described by the French mineralogist and crystallographer René Just Haüy in 1797. Long before that time it was admired for its vivid emerald-like colouring, caused by the presence of copper: the Germans call it *Kupfersmaragd* ('copper emerald') because of this colouring. It could perhaps be occasionally mistaken for an emerald, but its negligible hardness gives its identity away.

Dioptase most frequently forms columnar crystals of perfect cleavage in copper ore deposits. The main occurrences are in Katanga (Zaire), Altyn Tybe in central Kirghizia, Băita in Romania, Copiapó in Chile and Otavi in Namibia. Dioptase is not widely used, but is a highly valued precious stone; the transparent variety shows an outstanding dispersion of rays of light and consequent wonderful play of colours (known as 'fire'). The low hardness of this mineral is a disadvantage, because of which the cut and polished stones soon become 'blind'.

199   Dioptase — Altyn Tyube (Kazakhstan); actual size of crystals up to 1 cm

Rhombohedral; H. 7–7.5; Sp. gr. 3.0–3.25 g/mg³; for colour see text below; vitreous lustre, resinous on fracture surfaces; S. colourless

Tourmaline is the latest European arrival of all precious stones which are in current use. It was not until the beginning of the 18th century that tourmaline was brought from Sri Lanka (then Ceylon) by Dutchmen. Its name comes from the Sinhalese *turamali* ('stone attracting ash'): the stone has a very strange characteristic that was incomprehensible in those days. When heated, it attracts ash from the fire. Today, it is known that this is due to electricity, which originates in tourmaline because of its exceptional internal structure. When heated, the columns of tourmaline are charged positively at one end and negatively at the other. This phenomenon is called the pyroelectric capability of tourmaline.

The Sri Lanka variety is reddish to vividly red (rubellite). The less conspicuous black tourmaline (schorl) was known long before the Sri Lanka variety. European miners and stoneworkers were familiar with schorl in many localities, but its dull colouring did not

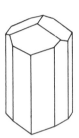

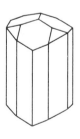

200 Rubellite — Pala, California (USA); actual size 10 cm

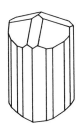

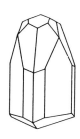

201 Dravite —
Dobrova (Macedonia);
actual size
of crystals 6 mm

arouse their curiosity. No one ever conceived that the pink turamali of Sri Lanka and the black schorl were an identical mineral.

The diversity of colour made tourmaline popular as a precious stone in ancient times. It is possible to judge from excavations and written descriptions that it was favoured highly in the past. But it was so often mistaken for other minerals that gradually it fell into oblivion and by the Middle Ages it was again quite unknown in Europe.

Chemically, tourmaline is one of the most complex minerals and its composition varies, for its different components can intermingle and replace each other: this, of course, makes tourmaline far more varied in colour than other minerals. Schorl is the most common tourmaline variety, whereas the colourless achroite is the rarest one. Rubellite, the most popular variety of tourmaline, has colours of varying richness and resembles ruby. Rubellite is chemically distinguishable by the presence of lithium. The green verdelite's richness of colour also varies, as does the blue indigolite's. The brown dravite

is rather scarce. Even in a single crystal there may be striking bandings of different colours (zonation).

Tourmaline crystals are columnar, usually long, with lengthwise striation, and have a triangular cross section. More frequently still, the crystals are needle-shaped. Tourmalines are very common minerals of granites and pegmatites, and appear secondarily in fluvial deposits. They are usually accompanied by pink lithium mica (lepidolite), beryl, topaz and apatite. At times tourmalines form rocks of a finely needle-shaped to granular composition, usually when closely associated with zinc veins.

202 Tourmaline — San Pierro, Elba (Italy); actual size of crystals up to 2 cm

The richest deposits of the gem varieties of tourmaline are in North American pegmatites. Perfectly formed columnar rubellite crystals were known, especially from the district of Pala in California. Today this deposit is almost exhausted. The most vividly colourful tourmaline crystals are found in the Italian island of Elba. Alternating bands of different colours often occur even in a single crystal. In Elba, crystals which have black ends but a green and pink core are a common occurrence and are called 'Moor's heads'.

Brazil is the home of the green variety, which occurs chiefly in pegmatites and less commonly in quartz veins. The eastern part of Minas Gerais state is the richest locality. The colour of the verdelites found in that area is not always constant, as is suggested by their commercial names, such as 'Brazilian emerald' or 'Brazilian chrysolite'.

Other notable occurrences are in Madagascar and in the Urals (Russia). The largest tourmaline crystals of gem quality are found, at present, near Muiiane in Mozambique. Their most magnificent specimen (rubellite), which is 42 cm long, is in the museum of Maputo. The largest fluvial deposits are in Sri Lanka. Dolní Bory (Czech Republic) has noted deposits of the black schorl variety.

As precious stones, rubellites are most in demand, especially those which resemble the ruby with their intense and deep colour. Verdelites are also very popular. In fact, all the attractively coloured transparent varieties make truly delightful precious stones. Cut stones which are vividly striped are considered a curiosity; schorls are ground occasionally into jewels for mourning. Otherwise tourmalines are most widely used in optics. The dark, transparent varieties of tourmaline are used in the manufacture of 'tourmaline pincers', used (like calcite rhombohedra) for the polarisation of light.

Chrysocolla - *hydrated silicate of copper,* $CuSiO_3 + nH_2O$

Cryptocrystalline; H. 2–4; Sp. gr. 2.0–2.2 g/cm³; commonly blue-green, blue, brown to black; greasy to vitreous lustre; S. greenish white

Chrysocolla, which in Greek means 'golden lime', was mentioned as a known mineral by the ancient Greek philosopher, surgeon and natural scientist Theophrastos (372–287 BC). At that time, chrysocolla was used as an ornamental stone. Strangely enough, it was not mineralogically described until 1968.

Chrysocolla usually occurs in thin coverings or encrustations, which resemble malachite in colour. It is distinguishable from malachite by the blue shadow. Chrysocolla originates as a secondary product of the disintegration of chalcopyrite and other sulphide compounds of copper. Limonite and opal often make it impure, or it is permeated by malachite. These were the very admixtures which made the exact identification of chrysocolla's chemical composition so extremely difficult. The main deposits are in Romania, at Eilat in Israel, in the malachite deposits near Gumeshevsk and Nizhni Tagil in the Urals (Russia), and also in Chile. Chrysocolla is not a particularly important copper ore. As a precious stone it is used only rarely (in Israel and Russia).

203   Chrysocolla —
Chiquicamata, near
Santiago (Chile); actual
size of detail 10 x 9 cm

Enstatite - *magnesium silicate*, $Mg_2(SiO_3)_2$

Orthorhombic; H. 5.5; Sp. gr. 3.15–3.176 g/cm³; usually greenish to deep green, grey-white, yellowish, brownish; vitreous lustre, sometimes pearly or slightly silky on cleavage surfaces; S. colourless

Bronzite - *silicate of magnesium and iron*, $(Mg,Fe)_2(SiO_3)_2$

Orthorhombic; H. 5.5; Sp. gr. 3.2–3.4 g/cm³; usually green-brown; bronze lustre; S. colourless

Hypersthene - *silicate of iron and magnesium*, $(Fe,Mg)_2(SiO_3)_2$

Orthorhombic; H. up to 6; Sp. gr. 3.5 g/cm³; usually black-brown, black-green to black; vitreous lustre, with coppery sheen on some faces; S. colourless

Diopside - *silicate of calcium and magnesium*, $Ca,Mg(SiO_3)_2$

Monoclinic; H. 6–7 (varies in different directions); Sp. gr. 3.3 g/cm³; usually greenish to colourless, darker when iron is present; vitreous lustre on fresh surfaces; S. colourless

Jadeite - *silicate of sodium and aluminium*, $Na,Al(SiO_3)_2$

Monoclinic; H. 6.5; Sp. gr. 3.2–3.3 g/cm³; usually whitish to greenish with different shades; slight vitreous lustre; S. colourless

Spodumene - *silicate of lithium and aluminium*, $Li,Al(SiO_3)_2$

Monoclinic; H. 6.5–7; Sp. gr. 3.1–3.2 g/cm³; colourless, yellowish, grey, pink to pink-violet (kunzite), green from the admixture of chromium (hiddenite); strong vitreous lustre; S. colourless

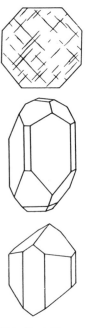

204 Enstatite — Bamle (Norway); actual size of crystals 4 cm

205   Jadeite ornament — Tibet; actual size 6.5 x 4.2 cm

Augite - *highly complex silicate of aluminium, magnesium, iron, sodium and calcium*
Monoclinic; H. 6; Sp. gr. 3.3–3.5 g/cm³; green, brown to black; strong vitreous lustre; S. grey-green

Diallage - *highly complex silicate of aluminium, iron, magnesium and calcium*
Monoclinic; H. 6–7; Sp. gr. 3.3 g/cm³; usually greenish; sometimes metallic lustre; S. colourless

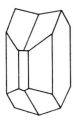

Pyroxenes are a group of important rock-forming minerals. They often resemble amphiboles. These two groups of minerals are very alike in chemical composition, shape of crystal and colour. Pyroxenes occur chiefly in igneous and some metamorphic rocks.

The orthorhombic pyroxenes form the so-called isomorph series, where the magnesium silicate and iron silicate substitute for each other. **Enstatite,** named after the Greek *enstates* ('resistant'), because of its behaviour when being determined using a blow pipe, occurs chiefly in massive form; the crystallised form is rare and usually imperfect. Enstatite often forms a large part of some basic rocks — either of igneous rocks or serpentinites formed through rock decomposition. Perfect crystals are found mainly in Norway. In all cases there is an admixture of iron; pure magnesium enstatite appears only in meteorites.

Bronzite acquired its name on account of its bronze-like colour. It is always massive, usually forming granular or fibrous aggregates.

Bronzite is found in serpentines, especially at Kraubat in Styria (Austria). It is used as a less common precious stone which, ground and polished to a lenticular shape, gives a conspicuous lustre.

Hypersthene is most frequently massive, in granular foliaceous form, of good cleavage; it rarely occurs in crystal form. It originates in gabbros, norites (igneous rocks from great depths), in basic extrusive rocks and in cordieritic gneisses. The norite va-

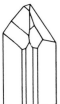

riety formed almost exclusively of hypersthene is found in the Labrador penninsula in eastern Canada. Cut and polished as bronzite, it has a similar bronze-like brownish lustre.

Monoclinic pyroxenes, in contrast to the orthorhombic varieties, do not form a continuous isomorphous group, but intermingle and replace each other in many different ways. It is therefore understandable that there are a great number of varied monoclinic pyroxene types.

Diopside derives its name from the Greek *dias* ('double') and *opsis* ('view'), because mineralogists had, in the past, two different opinions about its crystals. It forms short columnar crystals or granular aggregates. It is a typical mineral of contact rocks. The Indian variety of diopside, which exhibits asterism, is particularly popular as a gemstone.

The highly tensile **jadeite** was used a great deal in the past for making tools. It is usually massive, and microscopically fibrous, sometimes even felt-like. There are occurrences where metamorphic rocks are primarily formed of jadeite, and they are called jadeitites. Jadeite has long been used as an ornamental stone, mainly in China and Tibet. Many objects of art and rings are made from it.

The lithium-bearing pyroxene — **spodumene** — is obtained from North American coarse-grained granites; in Dakota crystals up to 12 m in length have been recorvered. Kunzite, a transparent variety of a beautiful pink colour, is of gem quality. The colouring is caused by the admixture of manganese. This precious stone is particulary valued and the sought after in America, where it occurs in the vicinity of Pala in California.

The most common monoclinic pyroxene is **augite,** which occurs in short columnar crystals, either embedded or loose in some erupted igneous rocks. In this form it is found in the central Bohemia highlands (Czech Republic), in Italy and Norway.

Diallage resembles bronzite in form, colour and lustre. It is an important rock-forming mineral in gabbros and serpentines.

Amphiboles - *highly complex basic aluminosilicates of magnesium, iron, aluminium, calcium and other elements*

Actinolite - *complex basic silicate of calcium and magnesium with iron,*
$Ca_2(Mg, Fe)_5(OH)_2(Si_4O_{11})_2$
Monoclinic; H. 5–6; Sp. gr. 2.9–3.2 g/cm³; green; vitreous lustre ; S. white

206 Spodumene (kunzite) — Pala, California (USA); actual length of larger crystal 6 cm

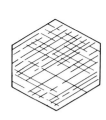

207 Amphibole in granodiorite, microphoto, Kozárovice (Czech Republic). Magnified 11 times.

Anthophyllite - *complex basic silicate of magnesium and iron* $(Mg,Fe)_7(OH)_2(Si_4O_{11})_2$
Orthorhombic; H. 5.5–6; Sp. gr. 2.9–3.2 g/cm^3; usually brown-green to green; pearly to vitreous lustre, glittering on some surfaces; S. white

Hornblende - *amphibole poor in silicon dioxide, containing a large proportion of trivalent iron and tetravalent titanium*
Monoclinic-pseudohexagonal; H. 5–6; Sp. gr. 2.9–3.4 g/cm^3; intensively black; vitreous lustre; S. grey-green to brown-green

Amphiboles, like other black minerals, were originally mistaken for tourmaline (schorl). The German miners called amphibole 'Hornblende', because it is hard to break and as tough as a horn. At the beginning of the 19th century this mineral was given its mineralogical name. However, even this name brings one's attention to its resemblance to other minerals, for *amphibolos* in Greek means ambiguous.

Amphiboles are rock-forming minerals which closely resemble pyroxenes. They are distinguishable by the different angle of their cleavage planes (amphibole approximately 120°, pyroxene 90°). Amphiboles most commonly form irregular clusters of granular, acicular or fibrous composition, embedded in rocks. In other instances, they are found in the form of columnar, smallish crystals. They are widespread in the mineral world and occur in many igneous rocks and crystalline schists. The amphibole group includes the industrially important asbestos, and also some precious stones.

Nephrite, the toughest known mineral, widely used as an ornamental stone mainly in China, is a variety of either **actinolite** or **anthophyllite.** Its exceptional toughness is caused by the interpenetration of minute fibres of these two members of the amphibole group. The most beautiful specimens of nephrite come from New Zealand and central

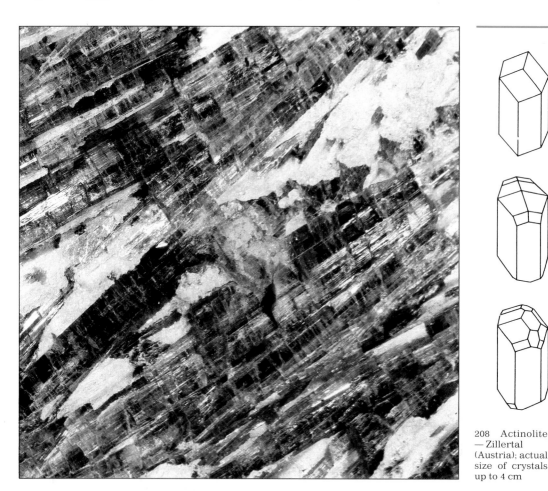

208 Actinolite — Zillertal (Austria); actual size of crystals up to 4 cm

Asia. Nephrite is one of the few minerals which began to be used very early in China, where the stone is very popular and highy prized. Originally the stone was quarried at numerous sites in the Kuen-Lun Mountains; however, today these sources are exhausted and forgotten. Only the boulders in alluvials still yield nephrite of good quality. Scandinavia is worth mentioning as an European deposit; from this region, nephrite boulders have been carried away by a glacier to northern Germany.

Hornblende (basalt amphibole) is an interesting variety, found sometimes in fairly large crystals of either short or long columnar form, usually terminated by three faces, similar to a rhombohedron. The crystals are usually perfectly bounded. Many rocks which are poor in silicon dioxide yield this mineral, especially igneous rocks of the Tertiary period (predominantly in tuffs and basalts). The beautiful crystals found in Bohemian deposits on the Vlčák Hill in the vicinity of Černošín near Stříbro, and in the central Bohemian highlands, chiefly in the vicinity of Lovosice, are world famous.

Common amphibole is chemically parallel to hornblende but contains less iron. Both these minerals are markedly distinguished from the other minerals in the amphibole group by containing aluminium. The most reliable method of telling the difference between the two amphiboles is to examine the colour of a thin section: hornblende is usually brown, whereas common amphibole bears various shades of green. In rocks both remarkably resemble augite. Common amphibole is widespread as a rock-forming mineral. It forms coloured components of many igneous rocks; occasionally it also occurs in metamorphic rocks. Amphibolites, that is, schistose rocks almost entirely composed of common amphibole, are very widespread among crystalline schists.

Rhodonite - *silicate of manganese and calcium*, $CaMn_4(SiO_3)_5$

Triclinic; H. 5.5–6.5; Sp. gr. 3.4–3.68 g/cm³; commonly pink, darker pink to red, turning black with weathering; vitreous lustre, pearly on cleavage surfaces; S. colourless

Rhodonite was established as a new mineral in 1819 and named from the Greek *rhodon* ('rose') on account of its rosy colouring, which darkens and turns grey to black with weathering. This happens because a crust of manganese oxides (chiefly pyrolusite, psilomelane, wad and their admixtures) are deposited on rhodonite's surface during oxidation. Commonly it is massive; the crystal form is very rare. Rhodonite is chiefly found in deposits of manganese ores.

Beautiful large pink pieces occur mainly in the Urals (Maloye Sedelnikovo) on deposits developed by deposition from waters. In these famous deposits the mineral is locally called *orlets*. Today, solid blocks of quality material weighing up to 50 kg each are recovered at Cummington, Massachusetts (USA). The Cummington rhodonites are popular because of their blood-red colour. Other noted deposits are in Langban and Pajsberg in Sweden (pajsbergite), Franklin Furnace in New Jersey, in California and, particularly, at Broken Hill in Australia, where crystals up to 10 cm in size are found. The compact rhodonites are used in the manufacture of many kinds of ornamental objects, especially in Russia, USA and Australia. Rhodonite is also very important as a manganese ore, for it contains up to 42 per cent metal.

209   Rhodonite — Franklin Furnace (USA); actual size 12 x 7.5 cm

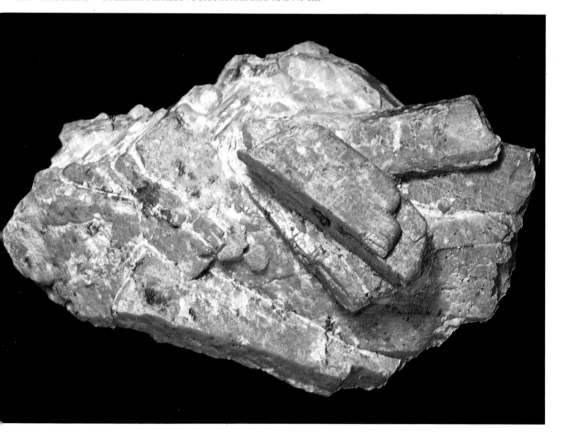

Pectolite - *complex silicate of calcium and sodium*, $Ca_2NaH(SiO_3)_3$

Triclinic; H. 5; Sp. gr. about 2.8 g/cm³; white; silky lustre; S. colourless

Pectolite was described in 1828 by the German mineralogist F. Kobell, from basalt deposits of northern Italy. He named the stone after the Greek *pektos* ('complex') and *lithos* ('stone'). Pectolite occurs in the form of finely fibrous radiating aggregates, composed of individual needles, on rare occasions ending in crystal faces, at the same time forming compact fillings of cavities and cracks in rocks. It is very similar to other white fibrous silicates, such as natrolite, tremolite, or wollastonite for which it used often to be mistaken. As a mineral it is not very abundant.

The main deposits are: Monte Baldo on the eastern shore of Lake Garda (Italy), Bergen Hill near West Paterson in the state of New Jersey (USA), the Želechov valley near Libštát in the foothills of the Krkonoše range (Riesengebirge) in the Czech Republic, southern Scotland, the surroundings of Langhorn in Sweden and the Zlatibor mountains in Serbia. Pectolite has no practical significance but its beauty makes it very popular with collectors, especially the West Paterson pectolite as well as that from Scotland and Bohemia, where magnificent specimens can be found. The Swedish occurrences are most unusual and resemble asbestos.

Wollastonite, named in honour of the English chemist, William Hyde Wollaston (1766–1828), resembles pectolite in appearance and chemical composition. Wollastonite is a triclinic calcium silicate, $Ca_3H(SiO_3)_3$, which forms white, finely fibrous to foliate-acicular aggregates. In contrast to pectolite it occurs relatively abundantly as a typical mineral of contact metamorphic limestones. The chief deposits are in the Banat region of Romania, in Pennsylvania (USA), Greenville near Quebec (Canada) and at Pichucalco in Mexico. In some places wollastonite constitutes the chief mineral of the rock masses. Such wollastonite rocks develop through contact metamorphosis of carbonaceous rocks with an admixture of quartz.

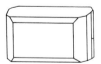

210   Pectolite — Želechov valley, near Libštát (Czech Republic); actual size of aggregates 3 cm

211   Apophyllite on natrolite — Ústí nad Labem (Czech Republic); actual size of crystal 2 cm

Apophyllite - *complex hydrous silicate of potassium and calcium with fluorine,*

$$KCa_4F(Si_4O_{10})_2.8H_2O$$

Tetragonal; H. 4.5–5; Sp. gr. 2.3–2.4 g/cm³; white, greenish, pink; pearly lustre on cleavage planes, otherwise vitreous lustre; S. white

Apophyllite was defined as a mineral by the French mineralogist and crystallographer René Just Haüy. He named it from the Greek *apo* ('away', 'off') and *phullon* ('leaf'), because it peels with heating, as water evaporates. This characteristic is also typical of zeolites, for which apophyllite used to be mistaken.

Apophyllite occurs in needle-shaped, columnar or tabular crystals, or in the form of lamellar aggregates of perfect cleavage. The cloudy white opaque variety is called albine, from the Latin *albus* ('white'). Apophyllite occurs fairly abundantly in cavities of basaltic rocks, phonolites, picrites (basic igneous rocks) and similar formations. The most important deposits are on the Mariánská hill in the Czech Republic, in the environs of Kaiserstuhl in Germany, in Iceland, at Bergen Hill in New Jersey (USA), and in Brazil, where it occurs in large crystals. Similar, perfectly transparent and finely coloured crystals are also found at Poona in India. These apophyllite stones are cut and polished for collectors' purposes.

212   Top: Pyrophyllite — Zermatt (Switzerland); actual size of aggregate 1.5 cm; and bottom: Talc — Zillertal (Austria); actual size of detail 5 cm

Talc - *basic magnesium silicate*, $Mg_3(OH)_2Si_4O_{10}$

Monoclinic; H. 1; Sp. gr. 2.7–2.9 g/cm³; commonly white, but whitish to greenish if containing a small amount of iron; greasy lustre; S. white

Talc takes its name from the Arabic *talq*. The name of its compact to massive variety, steatite, is of Greek origin. Both names are mentioned in very old writings, showing that the stone has been known for thousands of years. The so-called potstone (mixture of talc and chlorites) was chiefly used in the past for the manufacture of pots. The attractively coloured varieties of talc have always been a popular material for making ornamental objects.

Talc forms greasy, perfectly cleavable, flexible scales and plates. Small crystals of talc were found near St. Gotthard in Switzerland. Steatite (soapstone) frequently forms parts of schistose rocks. Talc is abundant in some deposits of crystalline carbonates, such as magnesites, in rocks rich in magnesium, and in crystalline schists. The USA is predominant in the world's production of talc, with deposits in New York state (carbonate rocks), in Vermont and Virginia. Europe's largest deposits are in Italy and Austria. Talc is today used mainly as a heat-resistant raw material, for example in the manufacture of refractory ceramic products.

Similar to talc is pyrophyllite, whose name is based on the Greek *pyr* ('fire') and *phullon* ('leaf'), for it tends to break into leaves when heated. It is found mainly in China. The compact varieties of pyrophyllite (agalmatolite) have been used from days of old for the carving of statuettes and decorative objects.

Micas - *highly complex basic aluminosilicates of magnesium, potassium, aluminium, iron, sodium and other elements; monoclinic*

Muscovite - *basic aluminosilicate of potassium and aluminium with fluorine,*
$$KAl_2(OH,F)_2AlSi_3O_{10}$$
H. 2–2.5; Sp. gr. 2.78–2.88 g/cm³; usually colourless, less frequently brown, pale green, yellow; pearly lustre; S. colourless

Phlogopite - *complex basic aluminosilicate of magnesium and potassium with fluorine*
H. 2.5; Sp. gr. 2.76–2.97 g/cm³; commonly red-brown; slight metallic lustre; S. colourless

Biotite - *complex basic aluminosilicate of potassium and magnesium with iron*
H. 2.5–3; Sp. gr. 2.8–3.2 g/cm³; usually brown to yellow, silvery and other colours, light to very dark (lepidomelane); pearly, slightly metallic lustre; S. colourless

Lepidolite - *complex aluminosilicate of aluminium, lithium and potassium with fluorine and hydroxyl*
H. 2.5–4; Sp. gr. 2.8–2.9 g/cm³; usually pink, mauve-grey, greenish, yellowish to white; pearly lustre; S. colourless

Micas represent a group of minerals which can be split into individual thin, elastic plates. This characteristic has made them highly suitable for many practical purposes for over three centuries. With their perfect cleavage and transparency, they were long used for window panes. Micas are very widespread. They occur as basic constituents of many rocks — pegmatites — for instance (especially muscovite) and as such they are often present in feldspar deposits. They are also abundant in other igneous rocks and in crystalline schists. Micas are important rock-forming minerals. According to their colour they are divided into light- and dark-coloured micas.

Muscovite is the most common light-coloured mica, and occurs mostly in the form of transparent plates. In other instances it forms only very fine scales (sericite) or even

213   Muscovite — Maršíkov (Czech Republic); actual size of crystal 5 cm

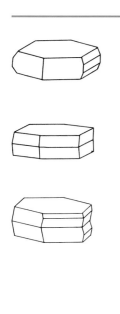

214 Lepidolite — Rožná (Czech Republic); actual size 8 x 6 cm

entirely massive formations. Muscovite crystals are rare. The fine, scaly form of muscovite is white, with a pearly lustre; the massive form is greenish. The largest plates of muscovite are found in the Urals (Russia) and in India.

Phlogopite represents the transition between light- and dark-coloured micas.

Of the dark varieties whose colour is caused by the presence of iron, **biotite** is the most common. Most frequently it forms imperfect crystals, which come chiefly from Monte Somma on the slopes of Vesuvius (Italy) and from Canada. The dark micas are not very resistant and, in contrast to muscovite, they decompose easily. Usually they change into chlorites.

Lepidolite, or lithium mica, usually appears in fine to coarse scales. Most frequently it forms aggregates in pegmatites. It was discovered for the first time at Rožná near Bystřice nad Pernštejnem (Czech Republic). The beautiful pink and green variety occurs there with pink tourmaline and topaz. The deposit began to be exploited early in the 19th century but mining stopped during World War I, though fine lepidolite specimens, usually embedded in vein quartz, can be found there even today. The chief localities of its occurrence are Penig in Germany, Alabashka in the Urals (Russia) and Hebron in the state of Maine (USA). Lepidolite owes its colour to the presence of lithium (this is why the rock is also known as lithium mica). Lithium is employed as an additive to various alloys, particularly lead and aluminium.

The current world production of micas is approximately 50,000 tonnes annually, the chief producers being the USA (about 50 per cent), and India (23 per cent). Light-coloured micas have a high practical significance because they are fire resistant and do not decompose in acids. They are used in electrical engineering for their insulating properties, and are also useful in optics. Dark-coloured micas have poor resistance to weathering, so that they are less useful for technical purposes. Ground biotites are used for the production of lithium; the admixed caesium is also sometimes extracted from biotites. Occasionally it is used as a precious stone; cut into the cabochon shape, full advantage is taken of lepidolite's pearly lustre.

Monoclinic; H. approximately 2; Sp. gr. approximately 2.6–3.3 g/cm³ (reportedly up to 4.8); commonly greenish with various shades, even black; pearly or vitreous lustre; S. colourless

Chlorites, named after the Greek *chloros* ('green'), are akin to micas, for they often form through micas' weathering. They resemble the micas with their perfect cleavage, but, in contrast to them, they are not elastic. If a chlorite flake is bent it does not spring back to its original position as a flake of mica does. Their most common occurrence is in metamorphic and metasomatic rocks. Some magnificent crystals are found in the Alps on the Swiss-Italian border — the chlorite found there is called pennine, which usually occurs in small bluish-green crystals, either separately grown or grouped in druses. Kämmererite, which is a pennine containing chromium, is an extremely interesting mineral. It forms tiny crimson to violet crystals. Recovered from its deposit at Guleman in Anatolia (Turkey), it is also cut as a gemstone for collectors' purposes.

Chamosite, discovered in 1820 in southern Switzerland by the French chemist P. Berthier, also belongs to the chlorite group. Chamosite forms oolitic (grain-like) aggregates of green colour with bluish shades; in this it differs from the closely allied thuringite, a green-coloured chlorite named after the deposits in eastern Thuringia in Germany. Both chamosite and the less common thuringite originate in rocks by deposition from water. They are found in Lotharingia (France) and between Prague and Plzeň in the Czech Republic. They are important ores of iron.

Cronstedtite (named in honour of the Swedish mineralogist A. Cronstedt) is a complex basic ferroferric silicate, crystallising in fine black-green to black pyramids. It forms through the alteration of pyrite. This comparatively rare mineral occurs at Wheal Maudlin in Cornwall (England), in Conghonas do Campo (Brazil) and in other localities. The most noted European deposits are in Romania and in the Czech Republic.

215   Pennine — Passo di Vizze (Italy); actual size of crystal 7 cm

Kaolinite - *complex basic aluminosilicate*, $Al_4(OH)_8Si_4O_{10}$

Monoclinic or triclinic; H. 1–2; Sp. gr. 2.6 g/cm^3; usually white or yellowish; pearly lustre, greasy on massive aggregates; S. white

Kaolin is a name of Chinese origin. The citizens of ancient China were working this mineral as early as in the 6th century. They ground it, mixed it with water and washed it, dried the fine deposits and pressed them into porcelain. For a long time they managed to keep the manufacturing process a secret, also the whereabouts of the kaolin deposits, which are in the present Jiangxi province. They were successful in remaining the sole manufacturers of porcelain until the 18th century, though porcelain was brought to Iran in the 10th century, and in the 15th century it was brought by Dutch merchants to Europe. The Venetians and the French tried in vain to learn the secret of its manufacture. Success came at last in 1709 to the German, J. Böttger.

Kaolin is a white clay, whose main constituent is the mineral kaolinite. Kaolinite is usually lamellar to earthy, with a greasy feel. There are also other aluminosilicates present in kaolin. This mineral resulted from the decomposition of silicates rich in aluminium, especially feldspars in granites and arkoses, which are sediments composed of quartz and feldspar. The most noted European deposits are in Cornwall (England) and near Karlovy Vary (Czech Republic).

216 Pseudohexagonal crystal of kaolinite from kaolin — Nepomyšl (Czech Republic); photo under electron microscope

Today only the very best kaolin varieties are used for the manufacture of porcelain. Those of a lower standard are used as fillers of paper stock and in paint manufacture.

Serpentine - *complex basic magnesium silicate*, $Mg_6(OH)_8Si_4O_{10}$

Microcrystalline, monoclinic; H. 3–4; Sp. gr. 2.5–2.6 g/cm^3; various shades of green and yellow, also reddish, striated or speckled; vitreous lustre, very prominent after polishing; S. white

Serpentine was already familiar in ancient Rome, where the Latin word *serpens* ('snake') gave the mineral its name, for it was the common belief that it could be used as a remedy against snake bite. Even fibrous serpentine — asbestos — was known in the ancient world. According to historical information, it was then mined in Cyprus. Asbestos' fire resistance did not then attract much attention and was not fully appreciated until much later. Objects and materials made from the mineral were

217   Serpentine asbestos (chrysotile) — Nová Ves (Czech Republic); actual size of detail 8 x 5.5 cm

considered more a curiosity than of any practical significance until the 19th century. Russia was the exception, for during the reign of Peter the Great (1689–1725) extensive tests with asbestos were carried out in an effort to make the most of the rich asbestos deposits in the Urals.

Serpentine occurs either in the form of serpentine asbestos, called chrysotile (from the Greek *chrysos*, 'golden' and *tilos*, 'fibre'), that is, finely fibrous serpentine, or in the form of serpentine rock, serpentinite. Serpentinite consists of microscopic fibres of chrysotile, tabular serpentine (called antigorite) and residues of igneous rocks through the decomposition of which (in the presence of water) serpentinite originated. The largest European deposit of serpentine asbestos is at Belangero near Turin in Italy. The richest world deposits are in Canada and the USA. Because of the finely fibrous structure, chrysotile is the most important of all types of asbestos (that is, finely fibrous silicates) used in the production of fire-resistant articles. Apart from being made into fireproof fabrics, it is used for roofing (transite, for instance), asbestos cardboard, and as insulating material against heat and electricity. The scrap material is used in various paints. Serpentine asbestos is a finer variety than amphibole asbestos. Massive serpentine is often used as building material. The precious serpentine (such as that from Snarum in Norway), with a particularly beautiful colour, is used as an ornamental stone.

Leucite - *potassium aluminosilicate*, $KAl(SiO_3)_2$

Cubic or tetragonal; H. 5.5–6; Sp. gr. 2.5 g/cm^3; grey-white; vitreous lustre; S. colourless

Leucite was already known to natural scientists in the second half of the 18th century. Their interest was caught by leucite crystals embedded in the Vesuvian lava, which

in shape resembled garnet crystals. They differed, however, in their grey or white colour. This is why leucite was originally taken to be a special variety of garnet which had lost its colour through the action of acid volcanic gases, or through the direct influence of the 'volcanic fire'. It was not till much later that it was proved that this is an entirely different mineral. A detailed chemical analysis showed that this was the first mineral known to contain a substantial amount of potassium, which until that time was thought to occur exclusively in plants.

The crystals of leucite are of a regular form, with twenty-four faces. These are not really crystals in the true sense of the word, but pseudomorphs of tetragonal leucite, which develops from cubic leucite at normal temperatures. Leucite is found mainly in young volcanic rocks. The main European deposits, apart from Vesuvius, are the shores of Laacher See, near Koblenz (Germany), at Loučná in the Bohemian Erzgebirge (Czech Republic), from which fragments of crystals up to 20 cm in size are known; other deposits are in São Paulo state in Brazil and Magnet Cove in Arkansas (USA).

218   Leucite — Vesuvius (Italy); actual size of crystal 1.5 cm

Feldspars (felspars) - *aluminosilicates of potassium or sodium-calcium*

Orthoclase - *potassium aluminosilicate*, $KAlSi_2O_3$
Monoclinic; H. 6; Sp. gr. 2.54-2.56 g/cm³; usually yellow-white or pink to blood red; vitreous to pearly lustre; S. colourless

Microcline - *potassium aluminosilicate*, $KAlSi_3A_8$
Triclinic; H.6; Sp. gr. 2.57 g/cm³; white to red (amazonite); lustre similar to orthoclase; S. colourless

Albite - *sodium aluminosilicate*, $NaAlSi_3O_8$
Triclinic; H. 6.5; Sp. gr. 2.62 g/cm³; usually whitish to colourless; vitreous or pearly lustre; S. colourless

Oligoclase - *albite with admixture of anorthite*
Triclinic; H. 6; Sp. gr. approx. 2.64 g/cm³; colourless, white, yellowish, reddish, greenish; vitreous lustre, often with goldish play of colours; S. colourless

Labradorite - *anorthite with admixture of albite*
Triclinic; H. 6; Sp. gr. 2.7 g/cm³; grey-blue to green-blue, with attractive play of colours, less commonly whitish to colourless; S. white

Anorthite - *calcium aluminosilicate*, $CaAl_2Si_2O_9$
Triclinic; H. 6; Sp. gr. 2.76 g/cm³; grey, reddish, white to colourless; vitreous lustre, pearly on some cleavage surfaces; S. white

Feldspars were named after the German *Feld* ('field'), because during their weathering and decomposition they release large amounts of plant nutrients such as potassium and in this way enrich the topsoil. They are therefore important in plant nutrition.

219 Feldspar (plagioclase in quartz diorite) — Krhanice nad Sázavou (Czech Republic). Magnified 11 times.

220 Orthoclase — Baveno (Italy); actual size of crystals 3 cm

There are two important classes of feldspars — potash feldspars and soda-lime feldspars, also known as plagioclases. The potash feldspars crystallise either monoclinically (orthoclase) or triclinically (microcline). The conditions for the crystallisation of orthoclase and microcline are almost identical, so it is understandable that a seemingly uniform crystal can be partly orthoclase and partly microcline. Both the minerals occur in interesting varieties and commonly contain an admixture of other elements, particularly sodium (if they are intergrown with the triclinic soda feldspar, albite). Plagioclases form a continuous isomorph series, with albite and lime feldspar (anorthite) as end members. The best known intermediate members, which are also the most important ones, are oligoclase, with a predominance of the soda component, and labradorite, with a predominance of lime.

Feldspars are usually cleavable, compact, granular or granularly lamellar, or they form tabular or short columnar crystals. Intergrowths of two individual crystals are common and there are many types of different twinning combinations, usually named according to their main occurrence. Orthoclase, for example, develops Carlsbad twins, Manebach twins or Bavena twins. Such intergrowths are less common with plagioclase minerals, though they have repeated twinning according to two laws — the albite law and the pericline law. With most feldspars, this twinning is often repeated and gives a series of lamellae, which are frequently microscopic. All feldspars are most commonly found in the mineral world in the form of twins or multiple intergrowths, where several individual crystals grow into each other.

Feldspar crystals usually have a perfect cleavage in two directions which are perpendicular or almost perpendicular to each other. In this respect they differ from other minerals. They are comparatively hard, and usually light coloured.

Feldspars are the most important rock-forming minerals. They are the dominant constituents of igneous rocks, such as granites and pegmatites, and also of far more basic rocks, such as diorites, melaphyres, porphyrites, basalts, and tephrites. In acid rocks potash feldspars are dominant; in basic rocks the soda-lime feldspars (plagioclases) dominate. But feldspars are also a vital part of a number of crystalline schists and sedimentary rocks, especially of arkose (sandstone composed chiefly of quartz and feldspars). Some cavities in igneous rocks, particularly pegmatites and granites, contain crystals of potassium feldspars as much as 1 m in length. They weather rather easily and are the basis of the origin of the rich kaolin deposits which are abundant throughout the world.

Feldspars, and particularly orthoclase, are important industrially. They are used chiefly in the glass and ceramic industries, in the manufacture of porcelain, glazing materials and enamels. Feldspar is an important ingredient in the manufacture of glass, for it supplies not only aluminium oxide but also potassium oxide and sodium oxide. Small quantities of feldspars are used in the manufacture of abrasives and materials of extreme hardness, which are used in grinding and smoothing operations; they are also utilised as cleansing agents (fillers of soap), in the manufacture of roofing, and in dentistry. Feldspar powder is used in fertilisers. Some feldspar varieties are cut as precious or ornamental stones, especially adularia, amazonite and labradorite.

The USA is the greatest feldspar producer (over 250,000 tonnes of feldspar material annually). The deposits are centred mainly in the states along the Atlantic coast (especially North and South Carolina, Maine), and South Dakota. Other large occurrences are in Canada, Sweden, France, China and Great Britain. Pegmatites yield all the feldspars suitable for industrial uses.

221 Orthoclase — Strzegom, Silesia (Poland); actual size of crystals up to 2 cm

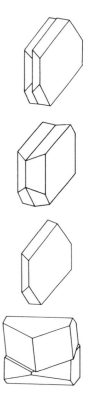

222 Adularia — Val Medel (Italy); actual size of crystals 2 cm

Orthoclase takes its name from the Greek *orthos* ('straight') and *klasis* ('breaking'), on account of its good cleavage. The thickly tabular and short columnar crystals are often intertwinned. The Carlsbad twins occur most frequently and are so named because they were originally discovered in the region of Karlovy Vary (for which Carlsbad is the German name) in the Czech Republic. Finely tabular crystallised orthoclase with an admixture of sodium is called sanidine (from the Greek *sanis*, 'plate'). It occurs in younger igneous rocks, such as trachytes and phonolites. Pure orthoclase is completely clear, but mostly it is white, yellowish or pinkish. The variety adularia originates from hot solutions and is the purest of the orthoclase family. It was named after the deposits in the Adula mountains south-east of Andermatt (Switzerland), where it occurs in cracks of Alpine rocks, just as in hundreds of other deposits in the Mont Blanc massif. Adularia is transparent, often permeated with chlorites, and sometimes displays a delicate play of colours. Its crystals, which frequently fill cracks in schists, are often bounded by perfect faces. In contrast to the other feldspars, they have a pearly lustre.

Orthoclase is one of the most widespread silicates in the mineral world and one of the most abundant rock-forming minerals. Not only does it represent a substantial part of many igneous rocks, but it also forms part of a great number of crystalline schists and rocks of sedimentary origin, such as greywacke, and other sandstones. In such rocks it usually forms tiny, evenly distributed grains. In some granites, orthoclase occurs abundantly in the form of large crystals, superior to the minerals of uniform grain size found in the rock. Such so-called porphyritic phenocrystals are often perfectly bounded and have the shape of flattened simple columns. Basically they are phenocrystals several centimetres long, from granite magma, which are older than the ad-

223 Adularia—Kandy (Sri Lanka); actual size of pieces approx. 2 cm

jacent basic substance and which crystallised from as yet unsolidified melt. Their crystal bounding is therefore more perfect than the bounding of potassium feldspars, which are a component of the basic finely grained granite mass.

During the decomposition (weathering) of granite they often fall out of the original rock and find their way into gravels and topsoils, where they are most commonly found. This is, in particular, the case with the Carlsbad twins, whose parent rock is the porphyritic Carlsbad granite. The twins are, as a rule, up to 10 cm long and have a rough surface.

The most exquisite orthoclase crystals are found in cavities of granites, where there is ample space to develop their shape regularly. They often develop in such cavities together with other minerals, both common and rare. Such coarse-grained parts of granites, which always developed with the influence of volcanic gases, are called pegmatites. In some coarse-grained granites, which originated with the action of volcanic gases, especially in pegmatites, orthoclase is often permeated with quartz. This is the origin of the so-called graphic (alphabet) granite, for quartz mimics the shapes of letters of the Hebrew alphabet. Orthoclase often mixes with microcline in graphic granites, sometimes even in a single crystal (as in the Ilmen range of the Urals).

The alphabetical intertwinning of feldspar and quartz, or the graphic structure of granites and pegmatites, is very abundant in some localities. Alphabetical striations are fairly common in the triclinic microcline (again, as in the Ilmen mountains). But they are less prominent in the triclinic feldspars, the plagioclases. If quartz penetrates into them, which happens only with acid plagioclase, such as albite or oligoclase, the striations along the cleavage planes usually resembles worms. Such a structure is called a worm structure, or a myrmekitic structure.

Orthoclase weathers fairly easily, often to kaolinite (as in the deposits at Karlovy Vary in the Czech Republic), or into clay or massive muscovite.

The best orthoclase crystals come from San Pietro on the Italian island of Elba, from Murzinka in the Urals, and especially from Madagascar, where in one locality a gem variety of orthoclase occurs, beautifully transparent and yellow in colour. Velké Meziříčí (Czech Republic) yields well-formed, nicely bounded crystals, as do Strzegom and Jelenia Góra in the Polish part of Silesia, Baveno in northern Italy and Scandinavia. The yellow and perfectly transparent orthoclase crystals from Madagascar are particularly suitable as gem material; they are frequently ground to many-faced cuts.

Feldspar crystals enclosed in siliceous monzonite (a rock similar to syenite) which occur in Grant county and the Carlsbad twins from Taos county (both in New Mexico, USA) are also large. Similar but smaller examples of Carlsbad twins are found in substantial quantities near Ray in Pinal county, Arizona; they occur in a pass which has been named accordingly 'The Crystal Pass'. The milky clouded variety of adularia, called moonstone, is a prized gemstone; after cutting and polishing it shines with a unique, beautiful bluish lustre of different shades. At the present time, adularia from Sri Lanka is particularly popular and is imported to European grinding plants. The stones are cut to a lenticular shape and their play of colours resembles that of the precious opal, though it is less vivid.

Attractive moonstones of gem quality are today also found in many areas in the USA. Beautiful white adularias, called valencianites, which form either simple crystals similar to the Swiss adularia, or twins occasionally reaching 2 cm in length, come from the mines of the Silver City district in Idaho. Most unusual specimens come, for example, from a new deposit on the western slopes of the Black Range in New Mexico. The crystals found at that locality are not of the adularia variety, but are sanidines, and often reach exceptional sizes of 30–60 cm. The volcanic region of New Mexico provides at the present time many other places yielding exquisite feldspar crystals with the typical moonstone play of colours.

Orthoclases with a delicate play of colours, resembling labradorite, are found at Frederiksvärn in Norway; their iridescence is caused by the interference of light rays with the delicate soda-feldspar particles present, which are enclosed in the orthoclase (so-called natronorthoclase). These orthoclases, like adularia, are cut to a lenticular shape.

Microcline was named from the Greek *mikros* ('small') and *klinein* ('to lean'), because of its triclinic symmetry, which can be recognised under the microscope. It closely resembles orthoclase, with which it is often intergrown. The blue-green variety is called amazonite, which is really a misnomer, for the green stone found in the

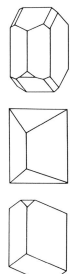

224 Microcline with crystals of smoky quartz — Crystal Peak, Colorado (USA); actual size of microcline crystals approx. 3 cm

225 Pericline — Sonnblick, Salzburg (Austria); actual size of detail 9 x 4 cm

deposits by the Amazon in South America is nephrite and not microcline.

Crystals of microcline are commonly large and perfectly bounded, flat columnar and very similar in appearance to orthoclase. This is because the conditions of crystallisation are almost identical for both these potash feldspars. Their crystals are frequently intertwinned, always according to the laws of twinning, never by chance. When magnified under an electron microscope, the two minerals show no difference in their intertwinned forms. This is because the symmetry of orthoclase is only seemingly monoclinic, being caused by submicroscopic intertwinned lamellae of triclinic microcline.

Microcline occurs mostly in granites and granite pegmatites. But there are also intrusive igneous rocks, composed almost entirely of microcline, and classified therefore as microclinites. Microcline is fairly abundant in the mineral world. The deposits most important from the mineralogical point of view are Jelenia Góra in the Polish part of Silesia, Iveland in Norway, where it develops in druses of pegmatites, in Finland, Miass in the Urals, and Magnet Cove in Arkansas (USA).

Deposits of blue-green amazonite are in Madagascar, in Virginia and at Pike's Peak in Colorado (USA), from where the most beautiful and most prized gem varieties are recovered. In Rutherford Mine and Morefield Mine near Amelia, crystals which were a component of the rock and which were 45 cm long have been found. Other attractive examples of amazonite come from the noted Canadian deposit in Renfrew county in Ontario. These are, however, commonly massive. There are known occurrences of perfectly bounded microcline crystals from Tawara in Honshu (Japan). They are up to 9 cm long, but are white and non-transparent. The richest deposit is Miass in the Ilmen mountains in the Urals, where it occurs in coarse masses, but also in magnificent crystals. The coarse-grained alphabet pegmatites in the Ilmen mountains in the Urals are composed of the blue-green amazonite and the smoky-grey quartz. According to earlier information, the average annual extraction in that locality was two tonnes. Amazonite was mined there with other local gemstones and with mica by Russian Cossacks in the 18th century, during the constant skirmishes with the local pugnacious Bashkirs and Kazakhs. There are some beautiful table tops made from amazonite from this period, which today still grace the chambers of the Hermitage Museum in St. Petersburg. The amazonite quarries in Miass are no longer worked, but one of them has been shaped into one giant amazonite crystal alphabetically striated with quartz, and is now a nature reserve.

Albite is the most abundant triclinic plagioclase feldspar; its name comes from the Latin *albus* ('white'). It is never a completely pure feldspar of aluminium and sodium, as is apparent from its chemical formula, but always contains an isomorph admixture of calcium. Albite crystallises in smallish tabular to short columnar crystals, often twinned. Elongated crystals, which are twinned in a specific manner typical of some plagioclases (according to the so-called pericline law) are called periclines.

Albite occurs in pegmatites, some granites, syenites and trachytes, always as a rock-forming mineral. In the crystal form it is found chiefly in fissures of various rocks. The main localities of its occurrence are Schmirn in Tyrol (Austria), Strzegom in Upper Silesia (Poland) and Bobrůvka near Velké Meziříčí (Czech Republic). The beautiful albite displaying iridescence (peristerites) found in Canada and Virginia (crystals up to 13 cm long) are used as precious and ornamental stones. They are ground to a lenticular cut.

Oligoclase, so named from the Greek *oligos* ('little') and *klasis* ('breaking') because of its low cleavage, is a coarsely granular to compact feldspar. It is exceptional to find it in columnar or short columnar crystals. Oligoclase occurs in granites, syenites, diorites, porphyrites, trachytes and andesites, but also in gneisses and serpentinites. It is comparatively abundant. The main localities of its occurrence are Tvedestrand (Norway), Monte Somma on Vesuvius, and the Urals (for example, Ayatskaya near Ekaterinburg). As a less common precious stone, it is ground and polished to the lenticular cut, especially the grey-brown oligoclase with distinct iridescence, which comes from Norway.

226   Amazonite — Pike's Peak, Colorado (USA); actual size of the large crystal 3 cm

227 Oligoclase — Tvedestrand (Norway); actual size of detail 9 x 4 cm

Two hundred years ago, a missionary called Father Adolf discovered on the eastern shore of the Labrador peninsula of Canada some rather strange stones. They were in large quantity. but of a rather dull grey colour, but when they were turned the colour changed into pleasing dark bluish and greenish hues. This discovery aroused exceptional attention among natural scientists, and after some time they identified this unusual mineral as one of the triclinic feldspars of sodium and calcium (plagioclase), and named it after the place of discovery, **labradorite**. Shortly afterwards it was discovered in large cleavable masses in other deposits, which also exhibited a beautiful change of colours — for example, at Kosoi Brod near Kiev in the Ukraine. Labradorite boulders were already being worked in 1781 in the famous grinding workshops of the town of Petrodvorets near St. Petersburg, to where they were transported from the Ukraine. The attractively coloured pieces with their marvellous change of colours were turned mainly into small ornaments and occasionally into jewellery. The local labradorites with their yellow, orange or golden shadows were particularly prized; in no other deposits do they exhibit such perfect merging of colours with movement.

The dark play of colours of labradorite, which is typical of this variety, is caused by the refraction of light from the microscopic crystal inclusions of various dark minerals, which are oriented in the direction of its perfect cleavage. These 'intruders' are most commonly fine scales or needles of ilmenite, magnetite or haematite, as has been established by a thorough examination under the microscope. As far as the lighter shadows are concerned, particularly the blue ones, it appears that these are caused by the reflection and interference of rays of light in the fine twinned intergrowths of labradorite, which can also be determined only with the help of a microscope.

Labradorite is most commonly massive, granular, and only rarely forms tabular crystals, which are invariably very small. Such minute particles were found embedded in andesites near Rosia Montana in Romania and also in the volcanic ash and tuffs on the slopes of Mount Etna in Sicily.

Labradorite also occurs as a basic constituent of various other igneous rocks poor in silicon dioxide, such as porphyrites, gabbros, diorites, basalt and diabase rocks. Often it represents a vital rock-forming component. An intrusive rock composed almost entirely of labradorite is called labradoritite. Labradorite also occurs in crystallne schists.

Apart from the deposits already mentioned, among which the Saint Paul deposit on the Labrador coast is still the largest and the most important, Ojamo in Finland is a heavily mined and well-known area. However, the occurrences in Finland seldom reach the gem quality of the labradorite from the original deposit. A new labradorite quarry has been opened in Madagascar, yielding the transparent variety called spectrolite.

Labradorite is without doubt the most extensively used precious and ornamental stone with a play of colours, which can be further enhanced with proper cutting and polishing. Today labradorite is mainly ground to a lenticular and tabular shape, or is used for the manufacture of popular and fairly expensive decorative articles. Labradorite rock is a useful raw material for building panels or in the construction of monuments.

The calcium feldspar **anorthite**, the end member of the isomorph series of triclinic plagioclase feldspars, always contains an admixture of sodium. Most commonly it forms druses of columnar or tabular crystals, frequently twinned. Anorthite is rarer than the other plagioclases mentioned. It occurs mostly as an essential component of basic igneous rocks, such as anorthosites ('anorthosites' is a term used for intrusive igneous rocks composed almost entirely of plagioclases). The chief occurrences of anorthite are on Mount Vesuvius, in the Urals and in the Antilles.

228   Labradorite — St. Paul, Labrador (Canada); actual size 10 x 4.5 cm

Sodalite - *complex aluminosilicate of sodium, with chlorine,* $Na_8Cl_2(AlSiO_4)_6$

Cubic; H. 5.5; Sp. gr. $2.4g/cm^3$; commonly blue to dark blue, greenish to deep green, green-yellow, grey, white, colourless; vitreous lustre on faces, greasy on fracture; S. blue-white

Sodalite has been known since early times; it is found fairly frequently in the ruins of the Bolivian city of Tihuanaca. However, it was defined as a distinct mineral only in 1811 by the British mineralogist, T. Thomson. Sodalite most commonly forms compact or granular aggregates, and on rarer occasions cleavable crystals, often twinned. Usually it is found in igneous rocks poor in silicon dioxide, such as nepheline syenites. Quite frequently it is an important rock-forming mineral, where it is often a substitute for feldspar. This is why, in petrography, it is referred to as the feldspar replacer.

The main deposits are at Ditrau (Romania), Serra de Monchique in Portugal, volcanic formations on Monte Somma (Vesuvius), Monti Albani near Rome, Rieden in Germany, Miass in the Urals (Russia), Kangerdluarsuk in Greenland, Ontario in Canada, the USA, Cerro Sapo in Bolivia, and Burma. In microscopic form, sodalite occurs in various trachytes, phonolites and basalts. It is used today as a semiprecious stone, usually ground to lenticular or tabular shape. Only the darker sodalites are popular, because they resemble lazurite in richness and shade of colour. The Canadian sodalites meet these requirements, and sometimes also those found in the USA and the Urals.

Sodalite often occurs with lazurite and possibly with other related aluminosilicates, of which there are quite a number. The best known of them is haüynite, named in honour of the founder of scientific crystallography, R. J. Haüy. As distinct from sodalite, it does not contain chlorine but sulphur and an admixture of calcium. It also has a higher degree of hardness and specific gravity than sodalite.

229   Sodalite — Timmings (Canada); actual size 9 x 6 cm

230 Lazurite — Bukhara (Uzbekistan); actual size 9 x 4.5 cm

231 Lazurite — Lake Baikal, Siberia (Russia); actual size 8.5 x 5.5 cm

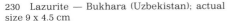

Lazurite - *sodium aluminosilicate with sulphur*, $Na_8S(AlSiO_4)_6$

Cubic; H. 5; Sp. gr. 2.38–2.9 g/cm³; commonly mauve blue, blue, mauve or greenish-blue; vitreous lustre; S. blue

Lazurite, or lapis lazuli, derives its name from the Arabic *azul* ('blue') and the Latin *lapis* ('stone'). It is most probable that in ancient times lazurite was taken for a variety of sapphire. This makes it almost impossible to establish when it was first used as a precious stone.

There are similar difficulties with information about the first known deposits of lazurite. Though many ancient works mention 'lapis lazuli', the localities of its occurrence and of its sale seem to be confused. However, lazurite's first known deposits were without doubt in Asia and in what is now Chile.

The earliest authentic descriptions of lazurite can be found in the works of Marco Polo (approximately 1254–1324). Marco Polo, who was the son of a Venetian merchant, travelled with his father and uncle across western and central Asia to China, where he stayed 17 years. He entered the service of Kubla Khan, who sent him on state missions, during which he travelled through many lands until then completely unknown to Europeans. He had opportunities to see lazurite deposits in the region of the upper reaches of the river Oxus (today's Amu Darya) in Afghanistan. It seems that even ancient Egyptians transported lazurite from these deposits, to be carved as amulets representing the scarab beetle. The inhabitants of eastern countries, especially China, carved many ornamental objects from the lazurite found in the local deposits. Though the deposits in question had been mined in ancient times, beautiful examples of 'lapis lazuli' are still being found there in irregular masses of lenticular shapes in marble.

The most noted occurrences of lazurite are, at the present time, near Lake Baikal in the channel of the Slyudyanka river in the Sayany mountains, where lazurite is found

232   Lazurite — Canada; actual size 9 x 8 cm

in the form of large boulders weighing up to 60 kg. The deposits in the Andes mountains of Chile also yield masses of gigantic sizes, which strongly resemble the lazurites of Afghanistan, but they are generally lighter in colour and mostly mixed with a substantial amount of limestone.

Other deposits are on Monte Somma (Vesuvius), where lazurite is found in erupted igneous rocks and in volcanic tuffs, similar to Monti Albani near Rome. However, these deposits have no real practical significance. There are more recent occurrences in the San Antonio Canyon in southern California, but even these are not of a particularly high quality. Some lazurite is recovered from the deposit in the Sawatch Mountains in Colorado, where the mineral forms dark blue veins and grains.

Lazurite occurs chiefly compact or granular, but the name 'lapis lazuli' is mainly reserved for the compact lazurite. In this case the name is not really applied to a mineral in the correct sense of the word, but to a rock, whose components are clearly distinguishable under a microscope. This usually is a mixture of white limestone, often dolomitic (speckles and bands visible to the naked eye), light-coloured pyroxenes and amphiboles, minerals of the sodalite-lazurite series, and pyrite grains. The parent rock of lazurite is most commonly a metasomatised rock containing lime.

Lazurite was and is popular as a decorative and precious stone. It is used chiefly as a gemstone for rings, brooches, necklaces and various carvings. In the past it was also used as paint (the natural ultramarine).

Natrolite - *hydrous aluminosilicate of sodium*, $Na_2Al_2Si_3O_{10}.2H_2O$

Orthorhombic; H. 5–5.5; Sp. gr. 2.2–2.4 g/cm³; white, colourless, yellowish to reddish; vitreous lustre, silky in fine fibrous aggregates; S. white

Natrolite was first identified in 1824 from the best-known deposit, the Mariánská hill at Ústí nad Labem in the Czech Republic. Natrolite crystallises in very brittle, fine hair-like needles, frequently grouped in radiating clusters. Less frequently it forms thin columns 3–4 cm long, or short but thicker crystals, ending in a low pyramid. The cross

233   Natrolite — Zálezly (Czech Republic); actual size of detail 12 x 9 cm

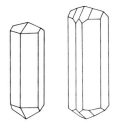

section through the crystal is almost square, so that natrolite could be easily mistaken for a mineral of the tetragonal group (it is pseudotetragonal). Natrolite is fairly abundant in the mineral world; it occurs as a secondary mineral in cavities of phonolites, basalts and other rocks. It is the most common mineral of the zeolite group. It will melt in the flame of a candle, and the water escaping in vapours expands its volume (a typical property of zeolites).

The main deposits are in the Czech Republic in the phonolite of the Mariánská hill, for instance; near Eisenach in Thuringia (Germany), in Auvergne in France, in Iceland and at Cape d'Or in Nova Scotia (Canada). The compact natrolites from Würtemberg (Germany) and Iceland are the only variety used as a gemstone. When cut into the cabochon shape, the Icelandic variety is known for its attractive and changeable lustre; the natrolites from Würtemberg are mostly used for making small ornamental articles, often with the parent rock. Crystals from some Czech deposits are exceptionally cut to multiple-faced shapes and as such they are kept in some collections. Collectors are very keen to have natrolite in their possession, especially specimens from the traditional deposits in the Czech Republic and Iceland, where they occur in association with other minerals commonly found in cavities of basalt and phonolites, especially with zeolites.

$$Na_2Ca_2(Al_2Si_3O_{10})_3.8H_2O$$

Monoclinic-pseudorhombic; H. 5; Sp. gr. 2.29 g/cm³; white to colourless; vitreous lustre, but fairly silky in the fibrous aggregates; S. white

Mesolite was defined as a separate mineral in 1816 by the German mineralogists Fuchs and Gehlen. It was named from the Greek *meson* ('centre') and *lithos* ('stone'), for, in chemical composition, it is an intermediate between natrolite and scolecite and is, basically, a mixture of them both, roughly in the ratio of 1:2.

Mesolite occurs in the form of delicate, acicular to hair-like crystals and fibrous to compact aggregates. Sometimes it is also earthy to powdery. As a secondary mineral, it is chiefly found with natrolite in cavities of basalts and in similar younger extrusive rocks. Mesolite is fairly abundant, perhaps more abundant than pure natrolite. Its occurrences are basically identical with those of natrolites. Localities: central Bohemian highlands (Czech Republic), Pflasterkaute near Eisenach in Thuringia (Germany), the island of Skye in Scotland, Antrim in Northern Ireland, Cap d'Or in Nova Scotia (Canada) and the Faeroes.

The largest mesolite crystals — needles up to 15 cm long — are known from Teigarhorn in Iceland. The most magnificent specimens come from localities in New Jersey (USA), where mesolite forms unusually thin white needles. However, the occurrences

234 Mesolite — Horní Hrad, near Ostrov (Czech Republic); actual size 10 x 10 cm

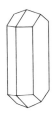

235 Scolecite —
Berufjord (Iceland);
actual size 15 x 8 cm

in the state of Oregon are the most unusual of all; there the fibrous crystals form thick, continuous masses with a visibly fluctuating lustre. Mesolite has no practical use so far.

Scolecite - *hydrous calcium aluminosilicate*, $Ca_2Al_2Si_3O_{10}.3H_2O$

Monoclinic-pseudorhombic; H. 5–5.5; Sp. gr. 2.2.–2.4 g/cm³; colourless, white to grey; fairly intense vitreous lustre, pearly on cleavage surfaces; S. colourless

Scolecite is, apart from clear calcite with its double refraction, the greatest mineralogical wonder of Iceland. Its name is derived from the Greek *skoliaxo* ('to bend') because when heated (for its identification) using a blowpipe it bends over. This is characteristic of all zeolites (hydrous silicates): they give off water when heated, which causes an alteration of their shape.

In appearance scolecite is almost identical to the clear or white natrolite. Like other zeolites, it occurs in cracks and drusal cavities of igneous rocks rich in calcium and aluminium, such as granites, syenites, porphyries, porphyrites, labradoritites and crystalline schists.

The chief deposits: Table mountains in Colorado (USA) and, particularly, the thick igneous rock sheets in the Deccan highlands in India. Many magnificent examples of scolecite have been found there, especially in the mountains of Bhore Ghat east of Bombay; many of them are known from the collections of world museums. However, the most exquisite specimens come from Teigarhorn near Berufjord on the eastern coast of Iceland. Scolecite occurs there in the form of wonderful crystal clusters in countless cavities and cracks of extensive layers of igneous rocks of which, in fact, the surface of almost the whole island consists.

236   Thomsonite — Pihel, near Česká Lípa (Czech Republic); actual size 12 x 8 cm

Thomsonite - *complex hydrous aluminosilicate of calcium and sodium,*

$$NaCa_3(AlSiO_4)_5.H_2O$$

Orthorhombic; H. 5–5.5; Sp. gr. 2.3–2.4 g/cm³; almost colourless, white, grey, yellowish, greenish, reddish; vitreous lustre, pearly on cleavage surfaces; S. colourless

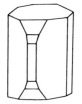

Thomsonite was identified as a separate mineral of the zeolite group by the British crystallographer and mineralogist, H. J. Brook, who named it after his friend T. Thomson. Sometimes it is also called comptonite. Thompsonite usually forms columnar or tabular crystals, usually grouped in radial clusters and bunches. In other instances it occurs in the form of kidney-shaped or globular aggregates with a radially fibrous composition and drusal surface.

Thomsonite is found fairly abundantly in cavities of phonolites and basalt rocks, more rarely in pegmatite veins. The main deposits include: Eisenach in Germany, Kilpatrick near Dumbarton in Scotland, Vinařická hill near Kladno in the Czech Republic, Colorado and Lake Superior in the USA. The best examples of thomsonite are today found in the northern region of New Jersey in the USA. These are white-coloured star-shaped aggregates up to 5 cm across, which in shape resemble stilbite. Radial aggregates composed of fine fibres occur at Peter's Point in Nova Scotia (Canada).

Thomsonite is occasionally used as a precious stone when ground to a lenticular shape. Thomsonite from Good Harbor Bay on Lake Michigan is mainly used for this purpose. At the Good Harbor deposit the mineral occurs as globular fillings of vesicles and cavities up to 3 cm in size. They appear chiefly on the lake shores, where they are found in the form of pebbles; they are radially arranged and are concentrically striated, with alternating stripes of milky white, yellow and green.

Stilbite (desmine) - *hydrous calcium aluminosilicate*, $CaAl_2Si_7O_{18}.7H_2O$

Monoclinic; H. 3.5–4; Sp. gr. 2.1–2.2 g/cm³; colourless, whitish, white, grey, yellowish, reddish, honey-coloured, less commonly brick red; strong pearly lustre on cleavage surfaces, otherwise vitreous; S. colourless

Stilbite is another member of the zeolite group. Its name is based on the Greek *stilbein* ('to glitter') and used to be applied to all zeolites with strong pearly lustre and scaly appearance. However, now the name is used only by the British and the Germans, whereas in all other countries the name desmine is used, which is derived from the Greek *desme* ('sheaf'), because of the characteristic appearance of the clusters of the small crystals, which are grouped in the shape of a sheaf and are radially lamellar to globular. Its apparently tabular crystals are always in twinned combinations.

Stilbite occurs in basalt and other similar rocks, in melaphyres and in amphibolites. The main deposits are: Kilpatrick in Scotland, the Fassa valley in Italy, Strzegom in the Polish part of Silesia, Kozákov in the Czech Republic, Poona in India, Iceland (where it forms crusts on double refractive calcite beds), and the Faeroes. The deposits in the extensive basalt sheets in the Deccan Plateau (Poona) southeast of Bombay are particularly popular: they yield large grey-white and reddish crystals and sheaf-like crystal clusters, which are considered the most beautiful in the world. Stilbite has as yet no practical use.

Similar to stilbite is heulandite; its only difference from stilbite is in the content of water – $(CaAl_2Si_7O_{18}.6H_2O)$. Often misunderstandings occur in connection with the name heulandite, for in earlier works this mineral was also called 'stilbite', which leads to confusion even today. As distinct from stilbite, heulandite forms tabular and radially foliate crystals in deposits of similar type to those of stilbite.

Another of the zeolite group, laumontite, $Ca(AlSi_2O_6)_2.4H_2O$, forms readily disintegrating white crystals and granular aggregates.

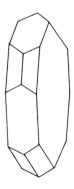

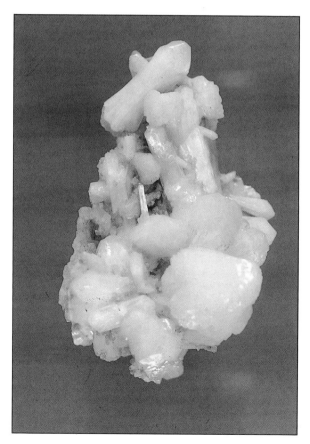

237   Stilbite — Berufjord (Iceland); actual size of aggregate 2 cm

238   Phillipsite — Vinařická Hill, near Kladno (Czech Republic); actual size 5.5 x 5.5 cm

Phillipsite - *complex hydrous aluminosilicate of potassium and calcium,*

$$KCaAl_3Si_5O_{16}.6H_2O$$

Monoclinic; H. 4.5; Sp. gr. 2.2 g/cm^3; colourless, whitish, white, grey to yellowish; vitreous lustre; S. colourless

Phillipsite, yet another mineral of the zeolite family, was discovered in 1825 and named after the British geologist and mineralogist W. Phillips (1773–1828). Though one of the most abundant zeolites, phillipsite occurs only in the form of minute, always intricately intertwinned crystals, or in globular aggregates, concentrically radiating inside. Phillipsite is a monoclinic mineral, but the development of its twins imitates the cubic system.

Phillipsite is found in basalts and phonolites as a secondary mineral, together with other zeolites. It also appears, but less abundantly, in some other recent extrusive igneous rocks. The main deposits are Stempel near Marburg in Hessen (Germany), Capo di Bove near Rome, the vicinity of Česká Lípa in the Czech Republic, and Richmond in Victoria (Australia).

Similar penetration twins are developed by another mineral of the zeolite group — harmotome, a hydrous aluminosilicate of barium, $Ba(Al_2Si_6O_{16}).6H_2O$.

Chabazite - *hydrous calcium aluminosilicate*, $Ca(AlSi_2O_6)_2.6H_2O$

Rhombohedral-pseudocubic; H. 4.5; Sp. gr. 2.08 g/cm³; white, red; vitreous lustre; S. colourless

Chabazite was identified in 1788 from deposits in Oberstein in the Rhineland. The name, introduced in 1818 by the German mineralogist, F.A. Breithaupt, comes from the Greek *cabazios*, which was used in ancient Greek poems to denote an unknown beautiful mineral. More recently, crystals of this mineral, up to 2.5 cm long, were found at Řepčice near Litoměřice (Czech Republic) by the Prague mineralogist, F. X. M. Zipp, and also by Johann W. Goethe.

The rhombohedral chabazite crystals are often intertwinned in regular combinations, forming lenticular shapes, called phacolites. Chabazite is found together with other zeolites, with calcite and aragonite, in cavities of basalts, melaphyres and, less frequently, in other rocks. The main deposits, apart from those already mentioned, include Strzegom in Polish Silesia, Iceland, Canada, Chile, Australia and New Zealand.

239   Chabazite — Maglovce (Slovakia); actual size of crystals 2.5 cm

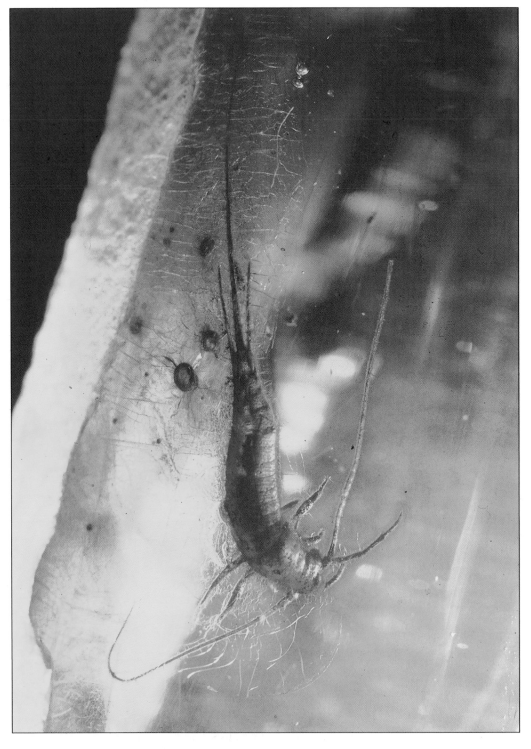

240   Amber with insect — Baltic Sea; actual size of insect 1.5 cm

Chapter 9

ORGANOLITES
(ORGANIC COMPOUNDS)

The organolite group consists of natural salts of organic acids, natural hydrocarbons (that is, compounds of carbon and hydrogen in various proportions) and fossil resins. Previously, all types of coal and petroleum were included in the organolite group, but now they tend to be classified as rocks. Even now, however, there are many substances which stand on the boundary of the mineral system, and are counted as minerals only by some mineralogists. Ozocerite, for instance, belongs among such substances. Others consider as minerals only the salts of organic acids, which in the form of minerals occur only rarely in the Earth's crust. These are compounds dependent on the Biosphere, but it is interesting to note that whewellite, for instance, has been found in ore veins. Organolites develop in the Earth's crust in various ways. Very often they support the rise of other minerals, which otherwise develop inorganically (sulphur, apatite, calcite, aragonite, pyrite and others).

Whewellite - *hydrous oxalate of calcium,* $Ca(C_2O_4) \cdot H_2O$

Monoclinic; H. 2.5; Sp. gr. 2.23 g/cm³; colourless to clear, less commonly whitish to grey; pearly lustre; S, colourless

Whewellite, with the form of its crystals and crystalline aggregates, its origin and chemical composition, is a rare and unusual mineral. Ancient miners saw it many times in cracks of rocks near coal seams, but they took it to be clear quartz (rock crystal), calcite or barite. It was eventually described in 1840 by the British researchers, W. H. Miller and J. Brook, probably from deposits in Transylvania, and named in honour of the English natural scientist, William Whewell.

Later it was discovered near Freital-Burgk and Freiberg in Saxony, and in some coal mines of the Erzgebirge basin in Bohemia. All the same, it was a great surprise to the experts when whewellite was found in 1906 in the form of magnificent crystals in the cracks of rocks in the Theodor coal mine, north-east of Kladno in the Czech Republic. Pefectly bounded and beautifully clear, whewellite crystals up to 4 cm long were found there in clusters measuring up to 10 cm. As time progressed, more occurrences and deposits were found in the Kladno area. It was ascertained that whewellite is a faithful companion of coal seams, and that it occurs fairly abundantly in their beds. Crystals from the Kladno area are among the most perfectly formed examples of this mineral in existence.

Whewellite is a typical mineral of coal basins, but it is never found in the coal itself. It develops only in its vicinity, either directly in rocks or in globular concretions of pelosiderites. Apparently it originated from solutions of calcium oxalate during coal formation, which is a simple process of leaching from the plant bodies from which the coal seams developed. Whewellite crystals thus formed everywhere conditions were suitable. It is an interesting fact that the biggest crystals always occur in fissures of rocks, whereas in the pelosiderites there are commonly small crystals accompanied by crystallised ankerite, barite, kaolinite and tiny crystals of some sulphides. Whewellite is the most uncommon of all these minerals and is also the last one to originate. Occurrences in ore veins are less common (Freiberg): in these veins whewellite is formed through the effects of calcium oxalate upon the adjacent minerals containing calcium.

241 Whewellite — Kladno (Czech Republic); actual size 4 x 2.8 cm

Whewellite crystallises most frequently in the shape of multifaced columns, or plates, and pointed crystals of various appearances. Heart-shaped or butterfly-shaped twins are often seen. The crystals are usually grouped in lamellar or star-shaped aggregates. Crystalline encrustations are very common. It is distinguishable from the very similar barite by the perfect cleavage in several directions.

The main deposits of whewellite are at Kladno in the Czech Republic and at Capnic in Romania, where in 1926 a crystal almost 7 cm long was discovered. Some crystals have also been found in Saxony (Burgk, near Dresden, Zwickau, Freiberg), in Alsace (Uberis) and in the Most area in the Czech Republic. Rich deposits have recently been discovered in the oil fields near Maikop in the Kuban region of the Caucasus (Russia). Whewellite is undoubtedly the most beautiful mineral of the organolite group.

Humboldtine, another oxalate, was so named in honour of the noted German natural scientist, traveller, geographer and geologist, Alexander von Humboldt (1769–1859). Also known as oxalite, it is a monoclinic hydrous oxalate of iron, $Fe(C_2O_4).2H_2O$. It forms elongated, seemingly orthorhombic crystals, and is pisolitic, fibrous or earthy. The crystal form occurs at Capo d'Arco on the Italian island of Elba. The similarly orthorhombic oxamite is a hydrous ammonium oxalate, $(NH_4)_2(C_2O_4).H_2O$. Commonly it is yellowish-white and forms a component of guano found near the coast of Peru.

Mellite is a hydrous mellitate of aluminium, $Al_2(C_{12}O_{12}).18H_2O$. The name is derived from the Latin *mel* ('honey'), because of its honey yellow colour. It occurs as white or yellow pyramidal crystals or is massive, granular or embedded in rock. It is found in sandstone and in coal. The main deposits are at Artern in Thuringia (Germany) and Malovka in the Tula region of Russia.

Dopplerite is a mixture of humic acids and calcareous humates. It forms reddish-brown greasy covers on bog and peat beds, where it develops through the oxidation of humic substances which penetrate into cracks among wood remains; with evaporation of water they concentrate and harden in these cracks. This mineral was first described as a 'gelatinous substance' from Austria by H. Doppler in 1849. Later the substance was named in his honour by the Austrian mineralogist and geologist Wilhelm von Haidinger (1795–1871).

Fichtelite - *hydrocarbon*, $C_{19}H_{31}$

Monoclinic; H. 1; Sp. gr. 1.03 g/cm³; colourless to yellowish; greasy lustre; S. colourless

Fichtelite was first discovered in 1837 in the peat bogs at Redwitz in Bavaria (Germany). The name comes from the German mountain range of Fichtelgebirge, where it occurred, or perhaps from the German word for 'spruce' (*Fichte*), on which it was discovered. Later, far more abundant deposits were discovered in the south Bohemian bogs, during the recovery of peat near Soběslav. There it occurs fairly commonly on the

242   Fichtelite — Mažice, near Soběslav (Czech Republic); actual size of detail 8.5 x 5.5 cm

remains of trees, especially on pine trunks and branches, which at some time in the past were swallowed up by the bog. Fichtelite forms lamellar aggregates, crystalline crusts and coverings, or occasionally elongated tabular crystals. Usually they are minute; only rarely do they reach 7 mm in length. Fichtelite is a delicate mineral, of perfect cleavage, greasy to handle and easily spreadable. Other fichtelite deposits are, for example, at Kolbermoor in southern Bavaria, near Sulzendeich by Oldenburg in Lower Saxony; in shaley coal near Uznach, south-east of Zurich in Switzerland; in the peats near Heltegaard, Denmark; and at Handforth near Chester in England. These finds provide evidence that rare crystallised minerals can originate even through the decay and alteration of organic substances — that is, plant and animal bodies.

Amber - *fossil resin*

Amorphous; H. 2–2.5; Sp. gr. 1.0–1.1 g/cm³; yellow to yellow-red; greasy to waxy lustre; S. colourless

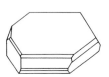

Amber was one of the most prized precious stones of primeval and early ancient times. Prehistoric man liked the stone because it was easily workable and attractively coloured. When polished, amber shone with a high lustre. Necklaces made of amber beads have been found dating from the beginning of the 2nd millenium BC, in the earlier Bronze Age. Simple amber ornaments were, however, made as long ago as the Old Stone Age (Palaeolithic period), as is

243 Amber — Klajpeda (Lithuania); actual size 7 x 5 cm

proved by excavations in several caves, chiefly in central and northern Europe. Statuettes of gods (idols), carved in amber by Germanic tribes, date back to the later Stone Age. Amber was also used as a form of currency possibly even in the New Stone Age, and quite definitely in the Bronze Age.

Ancient Assyrians and Babylonians were very fond of amber jewellery and even the Greek poet, Homer, in the *Odyssey* praised the beautiful amber. By then amber was correctly classed as a substance of plant origin, as mentioned by Aristotle (384–322 BC). The ancient Greeks even knew that when rubbed with a piece of cloth, it picked up small particles. This was discovered in the 6th century BC by the Greek philosopher Thales of Miletus. Later, when it was proved that this was the action of electricity, this form of energy was given a name derived from the Greek name for amber — *elektron*.

Roman women loved to dress themselves in amber jewellery, and amber

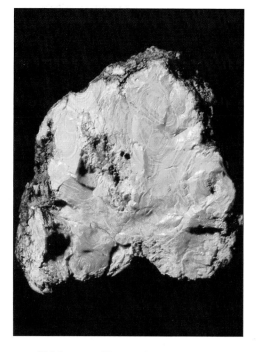

244   Valchovite — Hřebeč (Czech Republic); actual size 9 cm

ornaments had a high value. The great distances between the amber deposits and the borders of the Roman Empire made this stone expensive and desirable. It is known that Nero (AD 37–68) sent special expeditions to recover this mineral from the Baltic coast. The so-called Amber Routes led from the Baltic Sea across Europe.

Amber was an important item on the exchange market and was also greatly favoured by the scholars of Rome. The natural scientist Pliny the Elder (AD 23–79), discussed amber's origin and agreed with the opinions of Aristotle. The historian Tacitus (approx. AD 55–120) mentions how amber was used by the Germanic tribes.

The popularity of amber has survived through the ages. Amber jewellery was made in the Middle Ages, and even now is still in great demand. The most notable amber collection, dating to a relatively recent period, was the Amber Chamber, which was given by the king of Prussia, Frederick II the Great (1712–1786), to the Russian Tzar, Peter the Great (1672–1725). The collection was lost during World War II and has still not been found.

The fact that every European language has its own ancient name for amber shows how well known this mineral must have been even in ancient times. The Greek name *elektron* was used for the first time in the 3rd century BC by Theophrastus, a pupil of Aristotle. The name suggests 'lustrous metal'. Perhaps the clear lustrous yellow colour of amber, so enhanced with cutting and polishing, led Theophrastus to choose such a name.

The Latin name *succinum* is old too, and was the source of the later scientific term for amber, succinite. The German name *Bernstein* is derived from the word *brennen* ('to burn'), and reminds one of the easy flammability of amber. The English term 'amber' and 'yantar' in Russian and other Slavonic languages are also of ancient origin.

Amber is a fossil resin of Tertiary coniferous trees. Thick forests grew in the Tertiary period, and resin bled from damaged trees in the same way as it does today in our woods; but the trees of the Tertiary period were richer in resin. It flowed from the wounds and cracks and formed small drops or larger pebbles. These peeled off the tree

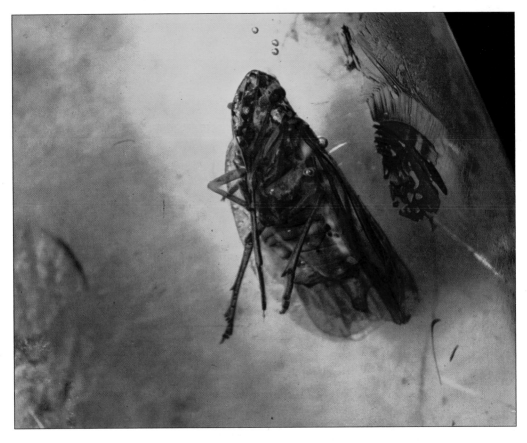

245   Amber with insect — Baltic Sea; actual size of insect approx. 1 cm

and dropped to the ground. As time passed they were covered with sediments. Many millions of years passed by, until erosion by water exposed them once more. Amber occurs as amorphous drops, irregular nodular fragments, grains, stalagmites and pebbles. It is usually cloudy, but sometimes translucent or even transparent; it is delicate and exceptionally light in weight. When heated, its transparency improves. The largest known boulder, preserved from the Baltic Sea deposits, is in the collection of the Natural Science Museum of Humboldt University in Berlin. The specimen weighs almost 8 kg. It is said that lumps weighing as much as 10 kg have been found on the Baltic coast.

In some amber nodules, remains of old vegetation and insects are preserved. Such remains from the Tertiary period, as much as 50 million years old, became trapped and glued to the flowing resin. These finds are scientifically very important, for sometimes the remains have been preserved in the minutest detail. They have to be studied enclosed in amber, for it is impossible to extract them.

The best known occurrences are of course on the coast of the Baltic Sea, where amber appears particularly after sea storms, when it is thrown onto the shore by strong waves. The 'blue soil' of the Tertiary sandstone is amber's parent rock in that locality. The largest deposits are north-west of Kaliningrad (Königsberg) especially in the vicinity of Yantarny (former Palmnicken). Amber is also found on the shores of Poland and Germany, and in Denmark, Sweden, Holland and eastern England. Baltic amber can even be found in many central European localities, south of their original deposits, chiefly in Silesia, where it occurs in rocks which were brought during the Ice Age by glaciers from the Baltic region. These are secondary deposits. Smaller quantities of amber have also been found in other localities, mainly in the Ukraine around Kiev and

Lvov, and in Romania, where there have been occurrences of amber nodules weighing as much as 3 kg. Strikingly fluorescent blue and green nodules come from Sicily, especially from the alluvials of the river Simeto near Catania; this variety is therefore called simetite. With its dark brown colouring it is conspicuously different from the Baltic variety. The conditions of origin of all these deposits were similar to those on the Baltic coast.

Fossil resins, which greatly resemble amber, also occur in the Czech Republic (Moravia and in the neighbouring regions of Bohemia). Such resins, which are classified under separate names, differ from amber chiefly in their geological age. They originated in the Cretaceous period.

Amber found at Valchov near Boskovice (Czech Republic) was named valchovite. Waxy yellow in colour, it forms fair-sized nodules in coal and sandstone of the Cretaceous period. In lignite coal of the same age, yet another mineral similar to amber was found — muckite. In contrast to valchovite, it is dark brown in colour. A pale yellow resin, neudorphite, was found later in the same coal.

Today amber is still widely used for the manufacture of various ornamental objects, though the time of its highest popularity (16th–18th centuries) has now passed. At present, amber jewellery is popular mainly in the Baltic countries where amber is recovered from the 'blue earth' strata on a large scale. Some collectors also pick amber from the more recent deposits along the coast or 'fish' it from the sea, using nets.

The amber which is recovered today is divided into groups according to quality and then it is worked, using special lathes. Many commercial objects, such as cigar and cigarette holders and other smoking accessories, and various souvenirs and ornaments are made from amber. The transparent variety with the pleasant colour hues is used almost exclusively for the manufacture of facetted jewellery, such as necklaces, bracelets and rings. During the manufacture of any works of art, full advantage is taken of the local colour shades of the particular amber, such as striations, merging of colours, or cloudiness, and also of the variety of form. Even the scrap from the amber raw material is not wasted. When heated under high pressure, 'compressed amber' (ambroid) is recovered from the scrap.

The Sicilian simetite is valued more highly than Baltic amber. The fluorescent stone, which it is possible to enhance still further by the right working methods, is particularly highly prized. On occasions, the resins from the Bohemian-Moravian border, so similar to amber, are also used as pendants or other ornamental articles.

Though the main use of amber is for making ornaments, this mineral also serves in the prcduction of succinic acid and succinic oils. Amber is also a good source of insulating material for delicate electrical instruments, and amber oils are used in medicine.

246 Amber — Baltic Sea; bracelet with polished oval stones; recent Polish work

247   Moldavites — Vodňany (Czech Republic); actual size of largest stone 4 cm

Chapter 10

METEORITES AND TEKTITES

This book has now described all the principal members of the nine groups of mineral, that is, inorganic natural substances which are chemically and physically homogeneous, whether they have been formed by organic or inorganic processes. Mineralogy, however, is also concerned with other inorganic natural matter, though they do not strictly comply with the definition of a mineral. Meteorites and tektites are such substances, and are in many characteristics closer to rocks than to minerals. Their composition and origin are also exceptional, and though they do not belong to any mineral system, they are extremely interesting objects. The study of meteorites and tektites can answer many questions regarding the composition of extraterrestial bodies, conditions in the universe and in the upper strata of the atmosphere, and the composition of the core of the Earth itself and it is of increasing interest to scientists.

Meteorites

These are the remnants of an extraterrestrial body which has fallen onto our planet. Today they arouse even greater interest because our knowledge of the universe has been greatly extended through space exploration. The falls of meteorites have, of course, always been the subject of mystery and even horror. In 1135, the Prague chronicle of the Canon of Vyšehrad states that 'A giant stone as big as a house fell out of the clouds on a plain in Thuringia. People living in the vicinity could hear the noise it was making three days beforehand. As it hit the Earth, half of the stone became embedded in the ground and for three days it remained red hot, like steel is when taken out of fire.' This description of a meteorite fall is somewhat inaccurate. All the same, it is most important, for scientists of the Middle Ages categorically denied that stones could 'fall from the skies'.

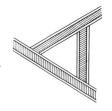

In 1754 the Prague astronomer Josef Stepling observed and described the 'shower of stones' which fell in the Tábor district of Bohemia. He was the first to state with absolute certainty that these stones fell to the Earth from outer space. Nevertheless, as late as 1790 the French Academy of Sciences of Paris voiced its displeasure and regret at hearing similar ideas, and accounts from eye-witnesses of actual meteorite falls were dismissed as imaginative stories. In 1794, the German physicist E.F. Chladni swept aside the old objections with definitive scientific proof of meteorites not being of terrestrial origin.

According to some current mineralogical experiments and opinions of some astronomers, meteorites are considered to be remnants of a large planet, which in composition and character resembled the Earth, and not just the core of the Earth, but also the surface layers. The planet moved through our solar system between Mars and Jupiter, and then for some unknown reason it disintegrated. Its particles are apparently still journeying through space. The fragments, when they reach about 80–150 km above the Earth, come into contact with our atmosphere, and because they are flying at the tremendous speed of 30–60 km per second, the air friction makes them red hot and sets them on fire. They flare up in the sky suddenly, like golden shining stars, which flash across the night sky. Only a few ever reach the Earth's surface, however.

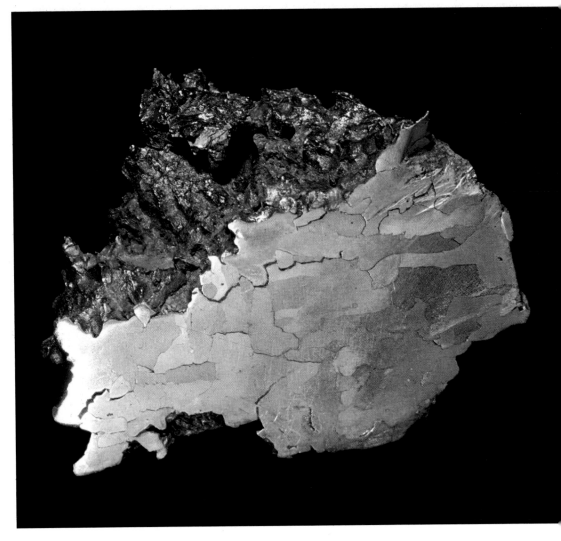

248   Iron meteorite — Loket (Czech Republic); actual size 16 x 14 cm

Meteorites are divided according to their composition into iron meteorites and stone meteorites. The intermediate types, formed by components of iron and stone, are very rare. Iron meteorites, which are exceptionally heavy, were the first to be found and are the most common. They are composed chiefly of iron with an admixture of nickel. As a rule, every iron meteorite contains two alloys, one rich in nickel, the other poor in nickel. When the meteorite is cut, and the sawn surface is etched with acid, the lamellae of these alloys are revealed. According to their structure they are divided into octahedrites, which have the lamellae rich in nickel arranged as an octahedron, hexahedrites, with cube-like structure, and ataxites, which have no structure at all.

Stone meteorites are inconspicuous and very like the Earth's igneous rocks. However, their surface is formed by a black crust, which is created by melting under the intense heat during its flight. Pallasites are intermediate between iron meteorites and stone meteorites. Basically they are composed of iron with an admixture of nickel, and olivine crystals are often found, usually rounded in shape.

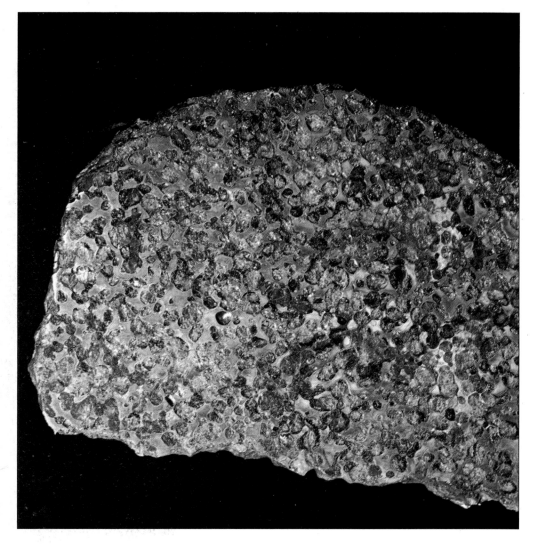

249   Pallasite — Springwater, Saskatchewan (Canada); actual size 26 x 14 cm

The largest known meteorite is a boulder which lies near a farm in the vicinity of Grootfontein in Namibia. It weighs about 60 tonnes and is guarded as a valuable natural monument. The biggest stone meteorite, which weighs over 1 tonne, fell to Earth on 18 February 1948 in Norton county, Nebraska, in the USA, as one of the components of a 'stone shower'. Meteorites seldom hit the ground as a single stone: they break into smaller pieces during their fall, thus producing the 'stone shower'. An example of such a collective fall of meteorites is the remarkable shower of approximately 300 meteorite stones which struck the Earth at Stonařov near Jihlava (Czech Republic) in 1808.

Some beautiful pallasites have been found in several localities in North America. In 1885, for instance, a pallasite weighing over 9 kg was found in Kansas in Brenham, west of Wichita. In 1931 three lumps of a similar meteorite with a total weight of about 68 kg were found in the vicinity of Springwater in Saskatchewan (Canada). The olivine grains, embedded in these pieces are as much as 4 cm across.

Tektites

These mysterious objects are today the subject of much scientific interest. The best known and also the longest known are the moldavites or vltavines, which are found both in Bohemia and Moravia (Czech Republic). They were discovered in the second half of the 18th century, and were at first thought to be olivine, then volcanic glass or vitreous slag from old glassworks. When several other deposits of similar glass were discovered, at the end of the 19th century, as far away as south-east Asia and Australia, it was generally thought that these substances must be glass meteorites. They were given the collective name of tektites from the Greek *tektos* ('molten') — irrespective of the locality of their occurrence.

Several new theories were then put forward. According to one, tektites were formed after a large meteorite had hit the Earth, melting the rocks where it fell, and scattering at the same time its glass particles in all directions.

Coesite, which is fundamentally silicon dioxide and forms only under high pressure, has been found in tektites. In contrast, bubbles found in tektites contain gas with a very

250   Moldavite (against light) — Netolice (Czech Republic); actual size 5 x 5 cm

low pressure. These conditions point to only one possible mode of origin: that at the time of impact of a giant meteorite on the Earth, the atmosphere is subjected to high temperatures and pressures, causing vacuum bubbles to form on the Earth and vacuum tunnels in the atmosphere. Tektites are therefore really the altered surface layers of rocks, which through the impact were partially melted down to glass, partially evaporated and partially recondensed. Then thermal currents dispersed these particles far and wide. This is why each tektite deposit occurs around a particular meteorite crater. The Ries crater near Stuttgart (Germany) is the place where the Bohemian and Moravian moldavites are found.

Moldavites and other tektites occur as cobbles, with noticeably coarsely wrinkled surfaces. They are dark green to green-black, but show a strong green colour when subjected to direct light. They are found chiefly in loose sediments in the vicinity of České Budějovice and Třebíč (Czech Republic). Moldavites were worn as pendants, or ground as precious stones. Even today they are a popular gemstone. Usually they are left in their natural state and are set in gold or silver.

251 Jewellery set with moldavites from southern Bohemia (Czech Republic); recent work; actual size of the pendant 4.5 cm

The moldavites industrially recovered at the present time in the only deposit in southern Bohemia lack the properties of precious stones. The same applies to other tektites too. They are not hard enough, damage easily, and often lack the necessary lustre. They owe their popularity to their unusual shape and the mystery of their origin. A moldavite found in Switzerland has, however, recently been accepted among the gem quality elite. During a visit, the Swiss government presented Queen Elizabeth II with a piece of jewellery in which a raw moldavite is inset in platinum together with a diamond and black pearls.

Many other tektites apart from moldavites are named after their places of origin: australites, javanites, indochinites, philippinites and thailandites, even ivorites from the Ivory Coast of western Africa, and georgianites from North America, and others. Many of these non-European occurrences are fairly abundant and the tektites from these localities are also used as gemstones. However, their surface sculpture is not as striking as that of moldavites, so they are usually cut only to a multi-faceted or lenticular shape.

All tektites are similar in chemical composition and appearance, but differ in shape and shade of colour. The primary difference is, however, in their geological age. This can be determined by radioactive investigation, by the potassium-argon method or by the method of nuclear (uranium) fission. In the first test the change of the potassium isotope to the argon isotope is recorded. The second test measures the traces left from the spontaneous decomposition of the atoms of uranium. It has been established that the North American tektites are the oldest (more than 34 million years old), and ivorites the youngest (1.3 million years). Moldavites are less than 15 million years old.

BIBLIOGRAPHY

Bancroft, P., *Minerals and Crystals*, The Viking Press, New York, 1973
Bank, H., *Aus der Welt der Edelsteine*, Pinguin Verlag, Innsbruck, 1973
Bauer, J., *Der Kosmos-Mineralienführer*, Mineralien – Gesteine – Edelsteine, Kosmos, Stuttgart, 1975
Bauer, J., Bouška, V., *Der Kosmos-Edelsteinführer*, Edel- u. Schmucksteine, Kosmos, Stuttgart, 1982
Bootley, E. P., *Rocks and Minerals*, Ariet Verlag, Frankfurt am Main, 1970
Chudoba, K. F., Gübelin, E. J., *Edelsteinkundliches Handbuch*, W. Stollfuss, Bonn, 1974
Del Caldo, A. et al., *Guida ai Minerali*, Fratelli Fabri Editori, Milan, 1973
Desautels, P. E., *Mineral Kingdom*, The Hamlyn Publishing Group Ltd., New York, 1971
Ďuďa, R., Rejl, L., *Minerals of the World*, Spring Books, London, 1989
Gebhart, G., *Das Große Lapis-Mineralienverzeichnis*, Ch. Weise Verlag, Munich, 1979
Hofmann, F., Karpinski, J., *Schöne und seltene Minerale*, Edition Leipzig, 1980
Kostov, I., *Mineralogy*, London 1968
Michele, V. de, *Dizionario di mineralogia*, Istituto geografico De Agostini, Novara, 1972
Michele, V. de, *Minerali*, Istituto geografico De Agostini, Novara, 1971
Pough, F., H., *A Field Guide to Rocks and Minerals*, Houghton Mifflin Co., Boston, 1960
Ramdohr, P., Strunz, H., *Lehrbuch der Mineralogie*, F. Enke Verlag, Stuttgart, 1967
Rössler, H. J., *Lehrbuch der Mineralogie*, Deutscher Verlag für Grundstoffindustrie, Leipzig, 1980
Schubnel, H.-J., *Edelsteine*, Südwest Verlag, Munich, 1970
Schubnel, H.-J., *Pierres précieuses dans le monde*, Horizons, Paris, 1972
Schubnel, H.-J., *Larousse des minéraux*, Librairie Larousse, Paris, 1981
Seim, R., *Minerale*, Neumann Verlag, Leipzig, 1970
Simpson, B., *Minerals and Rocks*, Octopus, London, 1975
Sinkankas, J., *Mineralogy for Amateurs*, Van Nostrand Reinhold Co., New York, Cincinnati, Toronto, London, Melbourne, 1964
Stalder, H. A., Heverkamp, F., *Mineralien*, Mondo Verlag, Lausanne, 1973
Strunz, H., *Mineralogische Tabellen*, Akademische Verlagsgesellschaft, Leipzig, 1982
Strübel, G., Zimmer, S. H., *Lexikon der Mineralogie*, F. Enke Verlag, Stuttgart, 1982
Švenek, J., *Minerale*, Artia, Praha, 1986
Vollstädt, H., Baumgärtel, R., *Edelsteine*, Deutscher Verlag für Grundstoffindustrie, Leipzig, 1982

INDEX

(Bold figures refer to main entries, figures in italics to numbers of illustrations.)

Picture Acknowledgements

Photographs 2 and 4 were taken with the kind permission of the Náprstek Museum in Prague, photograph 5 with permission of the Museum of Decorative Arts in Prague, and photograph 6 with permission of the Ethnographic Museum in Prague.
Photographs 8 and 10 show works from metals and gems by the professors and pupils of the Applied Art College in Turnov.

The majority of minerals pictured in this book come from the collections of the National Museum in Prague.

Zdeněk Borovec: No. 216
Vladimír Bouška: Nos. 244, 251
Archives of Jiří Kouřimský: pp. 4, 5; Nos. 7, 9, 14, 15, 19, 24, 34, 40, 46, 57, 62, 68, 91, 111, 116, 135, 166, 189, 247
Karel Neubert: No. 1
Dušan Slivka: p. 2; Nos. 28, 29, 35, 37, 38, 39, 45, 49, 54, 63, 67, 71, 87, 117, 120, 121, 123, 126, 127, 129, 132, 136, 144, 148, 150, 155, 156, 158, 161, 162, 168, 184, 190, 197, 204, 205, 208, 210, 212, 213, 215, 218, 220, 226, 239
Other photographs by František Tvrz
Line drawings by Eva Smrčinová